GENETIC
COMPLEMENTATION

GENETIC
COMPLEMENTATION

J. R. S. Fincham

John Innes Institute

W. A. BENJAMIN, INC.

New York   Amsterdam

1966

GENETIC COMPLEMENTATION

Library of Congress Catalog Card Number 66-10908
Manufactured in the United States of America

The manuscript was put into production on May 3, 1965; this volume was published on January 3, 1966

W. A. BENJAMIN, INC.
New York, New York 10016

EDITOR'S FOREWORD

This book is the third to appear in a series of monographs on Microbial and Molecular Biology. The purpose of this series is to encourage and sponsor the publication of carefully selected and edited short monographs on topics in the forefront of research in these fields.

Each book in the series will present a more comprehensive review of its topic, and a broader perspective, than is ordinarily possible in a review article. The presentations are intended to be sufficiently detailed, and thoroughly enough documented and illustrated, so that the advanced student will be able to obtain a comprehensive and up-to-date grasp of an actively developing area without having to refer extensively to original papers. To facilitate access to especially important experimental detail or theoretical development, reprints of key papers will at times be included.

These volumes are not primarily reference works, and they will differ from the traditional monograph in not necessarily covering every relevant reference. The rapid proliferation of the scientific literature makes it increasingly difficult for the experienced investigator, let alone the graduate student, to rely on his coverage of original articles to keep him informed of important advances across the general field of microbial and molecular biology. Hence the editor and publisher believe that appropriate reviews are of increasing value; and for this purpose it seems to us more important that the reviews be critical and lucid than that they be exhaustive. Accordingly, we encourage the authors to be selective, to speculate on immediate problems and on directions of future advance, and to editorialize in much the same way as they would in lecturing to their own students.

I hope that this series of volumes will be of value to the scientific community. Criticisms and suggestions will be welcomed.

BERNARD D. DAVIS

Boston, Massachusetts
October 1965

PREFACE

The great proliferation of work on genetic complementation that has occurred during the past seven or eight years has added a new dimension to the study of genes and of gene action. It has raised questions of great importance concerning the operational definition of the gene and the relation between the polypeptide chains, which are presumed to be the primary products of genetic translation, and finished proteins. Although it would be absurd to claim that all problems have been solved, at least the main outlines of the solutions now seem reasonably clear. The present consensus may be summarized by saying that allelic complementation is basically irrelevant to primary gene action, except insofar as it confuses the investigator, but that it is of considerable importance in providing an insight into the structure and functions of multimeric protein molecules. The time seemed ripe for a detailed summary of the field, and it is hoped that this short book will be helpful to advanced students, research workers, and teachers concerned with biochemical genetics and genetical biochemistry.

J. R. S. FINCHAM

John Innes Institute
October 1965

ACKNOWLEDGMENTS

Numerous friends and colleagues have helped to make this book as up-to-date as possible by supplying me with preprints and details of unpublished results. Among these, especial thanks are due to Professor E. A. Bevan, Professor S. E. Champe, Professor R. S. Edgar, Professor N. H. Giles, Dr. H. Gutz, and Professor U. Leupold. I am also indebted to the following authors and publishers for permission to reproduce figures: Dr. P. E. Hartman and the Editors of the *Journal of General Microbiology* for Figure 1-3; Professor E. B. Lewis and the Long Island Biological Association for Figure 2-1; Blackwell Scientific Publications for Figure 3-1; English Universities Press for Figure 3-7; Dr. H. Bernstein and Academic Press Inc. for Figures 5-5 and 5-6; and Dr. F. M. Johnson and the Editor of *Nature* for Figure 6-2. Dr. Hartman, Professor Lewis, and Dr. Johnson kindly supplied me with prints of their original photographs. Mr. L. S. Clarke, of this Institute, produced the photograph from which Figure 1-2 was made. Finally, it is a pleasure to thank Dr. D. H. Morgan for his critical reading of the entire manuscript in its first draft, and Professor N. H. Giles for a number of helpful comments on the final version.

J. R. S. F.

CONTENTS

Editor's Foreword   v

Preface   vii

1   GENETIC SYSTEMS FOR THE STUDY OF COMPLEMENTATION   **1**

     1-1   Organisms with a Stable Diploid Phase   1
     1-2   Heterokaryosis in Fungi   3
     1-3   Complementation Tests by Diploidy in Normally
           Haploid Fungi   9
     1-4   Complementation Tests in Bacteria   10
     1-5   Complementation in Bacteriophages   16
     1-6   Conclusion   17

2   FROM THE GENE TO THE CISTRON   **19**

     2-1   The Two Definitions of the Gene   19
     2-2   The *cis-trans* Position Effect in *Drosophila*   22
     2-3   Fine Structure of Genes in Microorganisms and Viruses   26
     2-4   The Function of the Cistron   30
     2-5   Genetic Terminology   31

3   EQUIVOCAL CISTRONS   33

    3-1   Redefining the Cistron   33
    3-2   Distinguishing between Genes and Operons   50

4   THE MECHANISM OF INTERALLELIC COMPLEMENTATION   62

    4-1   Complementation Resulting from Independent
          Action of Alleles   62
    4-2   Complementation Resulting in the Formation of a
          New Enzyme Activity   64

5   COMPLEMENTATION MAPS AND THEIR INTERPRETATION   90

    5-1   The General Incidence of Complementation   90
    5-2   How Absolute Are the Results of Complementation
          Tests?   92
    5-3   Different Forms of Complementation Map   94
    5-4   The Meaning of Complementation Maps   99
    5-5   Conclusions   112

6   THE POSSIBLE EVOLUTIONARY SIGNIFICANCE OF
   ALLELIC COMPLEMENTATION   113

    6-1   Theories of Heterosis   113
    6-2   The Occurrence of Interallelic Hybrid Proteins   115
    6-3   Possible Functional Significance and Evolutionary
          Stabilization of Heteromultimers   121

References   127

Index   139

GENETIC
COMPLEMENTATION

1

GENETIC SYSTEMS FOR THE
STUDY OF COMPLEMENTATION

Studies of genetic complementation, that is of the complementary action of homologous sets of genetic material (genomes), are of fundamental importance in the definition of genes and the analysis of gene function. Such studies depend on getting duplicate homologous genomes, or parts of genomes, to function in the same cell. A wide variety of different means to this end are applied in different organisms. No attempt will be made in this monograph to give any comprehensive account of the general genetics of the various organisms on which our present understanding of complementation is based, but it seems appropriate at the outset to make a brief comparative survey of the very different genetic systems which have been used so as to clear the ground for a more general discussion in later chapters.

1-1 ORGANISMS WITH A STABLE DIPLOID PHASE

In animals and vascular plants complementation tests present no problem. Homologous sets of chromosomes are brought together in the fertilized egg and remain and act together throughout the whole development of the individual, only being segregated into single (haploid) sets at meiosis immediately prior to germ cell formation. Any first generation (i.e., F_1) progeny of a cross between two different defective mutant stocks constitutes a test for complementary action of the two parental genomes. If the F_1 phenotype is nonmutant, or at least less abnormal than either parent, it is evident that each genome can make good, wholly or partially, some functional defect in the other. The reservation should be made here that, in animals, individuals of the heterogamatic sex (males in mammals and insects, and females in birds) receive an X chromosome from only one parent and thus give no information on complementation with respect to this chromosome. In mammals a similar reservation regarding the X chromosome may hold even for females, since here it seems that only one of a pair of X chromosomes is genetically active in each cell. As Lyon (1963) has shown, female mice, heterozygous for sex-linked markers affecting coat form or color, display a mosaic pattern, with some patches of hairs showing the activity of the one X and other patches showing the activity of the other. In this situation, X-chromosome complementation is presumably only possible insofar as it can be mediated by substances which can diffuse between cells.

Bacteria and the great majority of fungi do not normally show a stable diploid phase. Of the minority of fungal species which do so by far the most important are yeasts. In ordinary bakers' and brewers' yeasts (varieties of *Saccharomyces cerevisiae*) the diploid is the preferred phase. Haploid ascopores, the products of meiosis, are usually of two mating types (i.e., the yeast is *heterothallic*), and any two cells of different mating type will readily fuse to form a diploid cell which produces a diploid clone of cells by budding. Meiosis, with the formation of haploid ascospores, only supervenes when vigorous diploid growth is checked under conditions of starvation.

Complementation tests in *S. cerevisiae* are performed simply by mixing haploid cells of opposite mating type on an agar medium and observing the properties of the diploid culture which is produced. Where the strains being tested for complementation are auxotrophic mutants (i.e., mutants unable to grow on the minimal medium sufficing for wild-type growth), small drops of cell suspensions can be superimposed on minimal agar; subsequent growth indicates complementation and no growth, noncomplementation. Bevan and Woods (1962) developed a very graphic complementation test for classifying yeast mutants of the *adenine-red* type. These mutants require adenine and accumulate an adenine precursor which is converted into a red pigment. When drops of cell suspensions of various adenine-red mutants, all of the same mating type, were superimposed on a lawn of cells of a tester adenine-red mutant of opposite mating type, complementation was indicated by the appearance of white zones on a red background. When the synthesis of adenine was restored by complementation the red pigment was no longer formed.

A fuller account of the life cycle and genetics of yeasts, as well as of the other fungi to be mentioned below, can be found in the book by Fincham and Day (1963).

1-2 HETEROKARYOSIS IN FUNGI

Dikaryons. In most fungi meiosis occurs at the first two nuclear divisions following nuclear fusion, and the diploid phase of the sexual cycle is thus restricted to a single cell whose functions are limited to meiosis and spore formation. However, filamentous fungi of the two major groups Ascomycetes and Basidiomycetes have, as a regular part of their sexual life cycle, a *dikaryotic* phase in which pairs of nuclei, often of different and compatible mating type, are associated but not fused in each cell of the mycelium. In the Ascomycetes, including the important experimental organisms *Neurospora crassa* and *Aspergillus nidulans,* this dikaryotic phase occurs only within the developing fruit body (perithecium) in the interval between fertilization and nuclear fusion, and it cannot be cultured as a free-living mycelium. On the other hand, in most Basidiomycetes free vegetative growth tends to be dikaryotic, with a pair of nuclei of opposite mating type in each cell. Two species of Hymenomycetes (the mushroom-toadstool subdivision of the Basidiomycetes) which have been used quite extensively as genetic organisms are *Coprinus lagopus* and *Schizophyllum commune.* In each of these species haploid spores released from the fruit body following meiosis germinate to give septate mycelia having one haploid nucleus per cell (i.e., *monokaryons*). The monokaryons from one fruiting body can be classified into four self-sterile mating types. When monokaryons of different and compatible mating types happen to grow together, fusions of hyphae immediately occur and a dikaryon is formed in which each cell is binucleate, containing one haploid nucleus of each type. The dikaryon is distinguishable by its characteristic *clamp connections,* which are a consequence of the curious mechanism of cell division which ensures that each daughter cell receives one of each kind of nucleus (Figure 1-1). A hymenomycete dikaryon is more vigorous than a monokaryon and can make extensive growth either

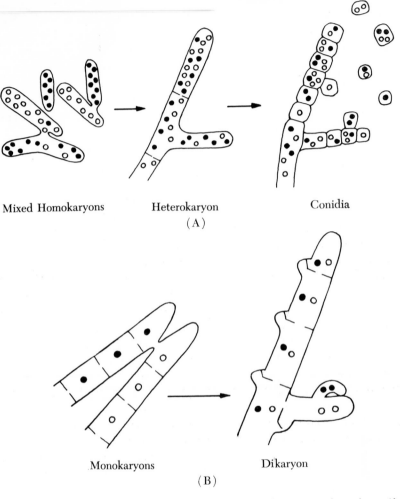

Mixed Homokaryons   Heterokaryon   Conidia

(A)

Monokaryons   Dikaryon

(B)

FIGURE 1-1   Formation of a heterokaryon from two homokaryotic
types of germinating conidia in *Neurospora crassa* (A) and
of a dikaryon from two monokaryons in a hymenomycete
such as *Coprinus lagopus*. (B). Genetically different nuclei
are shown as open and closed circles (semidiagrammatic).

on natural or synthetic media. Under favorable conditions it forms
fruit bodies in which fusions of the pairs of nuclei occur, followed by
meiosis and spore formation. Hymenomycete dikaryons have not
been very much used in studies of complementation but are very
suitable for such investigations. One of their advantages is that the

nuclear ratio is always one-to-one, and one thus has a more accurately controlled if less flexible system than is provided by heterokaryosis in *Neurospora,* considered later. Their only slightly inconvenient feature is that they have to be made from strains of different and compatible mating types, and this may necessitate a certain amount of preliminary breeding.

Two other groups of Basidiomycetes, the smuts (Ustilaginales) and the rusts (Uredinales) also have dikaryotic phases of major importance in their life histories, but in both groups the obligatorily parasitic nature of the dikaryon limits its experimental usefulness.

Heterokaryons in coenocytic fungi. In *Neurospora crassa,* as well as in numerous other filamentous fungi in which a dikaryotic phase capable of independent growth is not available, complementation tests are readily made through the use of heterokaryons which are formed as the result of fusions between hyphae of different genotypes. In most Ascomycetes (as well as in the Phycomycetes, an important group whose genetics are relatively unexplored) the mycelium is not subdivided into cells each with a fixed number of nuclei. Although in Ascomycetes, the hyphae are subdivided by crosswalls (septa), the compartments between the septa tend to contain rather large and variable numbers of nuclei, and the septa have central pores through which both cytoplasm and nuclei can pass relatively freely. In Phycomycetes there are no septa. A heterokaryon will tend to have its two kinds of nuclei closely intermingled, but in no fixed proportion to each other. This may be described as a *coenocytic* rather than a strictly cellular type of organization.

In *Neurospora crassa,* where the matter has been most thoroughly investigated, stable heterokaryons can only be formed when the component strains are of the same mating type. Stable heterokaryosis also requires that the two participating nuclei be similar with respect to at least two other genes. Combinations of different alleles of these compatibility genes can lead to cytoplasmic degeneration and death of the heterokaryotic hyphal compartments (Garnjobst, 1953, 1955; Garnjobst and Wilson, 1956). Such incompatibility is often a troublesome obstacle to studies on heterokaryons, especially between mutants originating from different wild-type stocks, but it can usually be overcome by a short program of inbreeding.

It is generally assumed that when two auxotrophic strains can each form a prototrophic heterokaryon with a third, they are capable of forming a stable heterokaryon with each other. There is no doubt that such an assumption is usually valid, but it may occasionally fail. De Serres (1962) found that a small minority of newly induced auxotrophs seemed to carry newly arisen incompatibility factors which caused failure of heterokaryon formation in certain specific combinations. Thus *complete* reliance cannot be placed upon a negative complementation test between two newly induced mutants, even when they have come from the same wild-type stock. In the related *secondarily homothallic* species N. *tetrasperma*, in which two nuclei of opposite mating type are regularly segregated into each ascospore, the vegetative mycelium is almost always heterokaryotic with respect to mating type, and is consequently self-fertile. In this species, unlike N. *crassa* and the other normally heterothallic species, mating type exercises no restriction on hetero-karyon formation.

An important difference between *Neurospora* heterokaryons and a hymenomycete dikaryon is that while the latter has its two differ-ent genomes in a fixed one-to-one ratio (in this respect resembling a diploid), the nuclear ratio in the former is infinitely variable. Experi-mentally it is possible to set up heterokaryons from the same two *Neurospora* strains, but with widely differing nuclear ratios, by inoc-ulating different ratios of conidia (asexual spores) in dense mixtures on to agar medium. Once a heterokaryon is established through the fusing together of conidial germ tubes, which happens very rapidly with compatible strains, its nuclear ratio tends to be rather stable during further growth even if it is not the one which would give the fastest growth rate (Pittenger, Kimball, and Atwood, 1955). This seems most easily explained by supposing that the nuclei pass-ing into each new hyphal branch are sufficiently numerous for fluctu-ations in ratio due to statistical sampling to be generally unim-portant.

Complementation tests have been carried out more extensively in N. *crassa* than in any other organism, almost always with auxo-trophic mutants (Beadle and Coonradt, 1944). The usual method is simply to superimpose small inocula of conidia of the two strains under test at a marked point on a plate of minimal agar medium, with the usual sucrose or glucose partly replaced by sorbose to bring about a tight colonial type of growth conducive to easy scor-ing. The auxotrophic conidia in a moderately dense mixed inoculum can always grow enough on the basis of their own reserves to form a heterokaryotic mycelium, after which growth will usually stop, if the mutants are noncomplementary, or continue indefinitely at more or less wild-type rate if they are complementary (Figure 1-2). Fully complementary and compatible strains will usually be seen to be growing strongly after 1 day at 25°C, but imperfectly complemen-

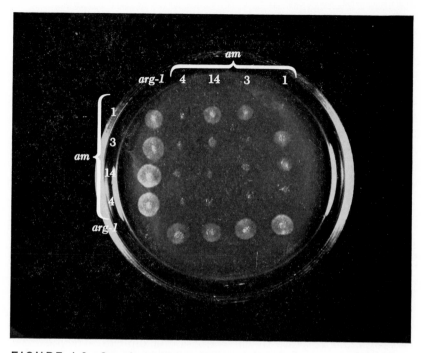

FIGURE 1-2   Complementation tests in *Neurospora crassa* (see text).
The five strains shown tested in all pairwise combinations
carry, respectively, four allelic mutations at the *am* locus
(cf. Figure 5-3) and the nonallelic mutation *arg-1*. The *am*[14]
+*am*[3] pair shows complementation which is comparatively weak.

tary allelic mutants may have to be incubated for as long as 5 or 6
days before showing a positive result.

In this kind of test it is not usual to attempt any precise control
over the nuclear ratio of the heterokaryon formed. In principle
certain combinations of mutants might be complementary only within a narrow range of nuclear ratio, but in practice variable results,
which could be ascribed to a strong effect of nuclear ratio, seem to
be uncommon. So long as the two kinds of conidia are mixed in proportions which are not grossly unequal results seem to be reproducible. It is always possible to check the nuclear ratio after the
event by determining the proportions of the two kinds of homokaryotic conidia formed on the heterokaryon. Although most conidia
are usually multinucleate, a proportion are uninucleate, while most of
the others have small numbers (2–10) of nuclei and thus stand a good

chance of being homokaryotic. The ratio of the two types of homokaryotic conidia should reflect the ratio of the two types of nuclei in
the original heterokaryon.

Complementation tests on auxotrophic *Neurospora* mutants can
also be made by inoculating mixed conidia in known numbers into
a standard quantity of liquid minimal medium (Brockman and De
Serres, 1963). In liquid medium the opportunities for anastomosis
of germinating conidia are presumably more limited than on a heavily inoculated agar surface, and so a positive response may be longer
delayed, but this method can give very reproducible results as regards the time at which visible growth appears.

In *Aspergillus nidulans* heterokaryons are rather more troublesome
to isolate (Pontecorvo *et al.*, 1953). Mixed inoculation of conidia onto
an agar surface does not, as in *Neurospora*, lead to the formation
of heterokaryotic mycelium over the whole area inoculated, but only
at isolated points. It seems that hyphal anastomosis occurs much
less readily in *Aspergillus* than in *Neurospora*. Even when an *Aspergillus* heterokaryon is formed from fully complementary mutants
its growth is never as strong as that of the wild-type fungus, perhaps
because the nuclei are not intermingled as closely as they are in
Neurospora. Consequently the formation of diploids, which can be
readily achieved by selective methods (see discussion later), is rather
more satisfactory for complementation tests in *Aspergillus* than is
heterokaryosis.

Pseudowild types in *Neurospora*. When a cross is made between two *Neurospora* strains carrying complementary mutations at
closely linked loci, some nonmutant ascospores will normally be produced as a result of ordinary genetic recombination during meiosis.
In addition, as Pittenger (1954) showed, a small proportion (about
10^{-3} or 10^{-4}) of the ascospores from such a cross are nonmutant in
phenotype because they contain *both* mutant chromosomes, one
from each parent. Such ascospores seem to originate from nuclei
which are diploid with respect to just one of the seven chromosomes
—in other words, they are *disomic*. The two homologous chromosomes appear to be segregated into different nuclei either at the very
first mitotic division after the formation of the ascospore or soon
after ascospore germination, since the cultures given by pseudowild
spores are in all respects indistinguishable from ordinary heterokaryons, usually carrying two kinds of nuclei in a one-to-one ratio.
Disomy, leading to heterokaryosis, can occur for each of the seven
linkage groups, but generally only for one at a time. It is a sufficiently frequent and constant phenomenon to constitute a reliable

test for complementation of any two mutants which recombine at a low enough frequency for true wild types to be infrequent relative to pseudowilds if the latter occur. In fact, pseudowild formation sometimes gives a clearer indication of complementation than the more usual test by heterokaryon formation (De Serres, 1960; Case and Giles, 1960). One reason for this may be the assured one-to-one nuclear ratio in a pseudowild mycelium. Another is probably that the two different kinds of nuclei in a pseudowild mycelium are *identical* with respect to six of the seven chromosomes and are thus likely to be perfectly compatible in a heterokaryon. It is suspected that many incompatibility factors may exist which may normally have small or negligible effects, but which may tip the balance against growth when the degree of complementation is in any case slight.

1-3 COMPLEMENTATION TESTS BY DIPLOIDY IN NORMALLY HAPLOID FUNGI

Roper (1952) was the first to isolate diploid strains from a normally haploid fungus. His method depended on the fact that *Aspergillus* conidia are all uninucleate. The procedure is first to make a heterokaryon from two haploid strains carrying complementary mutations (either auxotrophic mutants or mutants with defective pigmentation), and then to select apparently wild-type conidia formed on the heterokaryon. When the original mutants are auxotrophs one can select automatically for prototrophs by spreading the conidia on minimal medium, while in the case of pigment mutants it is necessary to select normally pigmented colonies by eye. In either case the selected colonies, showing complementary action of the two original mutant genomes, are generally found to be diploid. Evidently nuclear fusion occurs with low frequency in vegetative mycelium of *Aspergillus*, with the result that one conidium in 10^{-6} or 10^{-7} is diploid. *Aspergillus* diploids are comparable to haploids in growth rate and general vigor. For complementation tests it is best to select diploids by reference to marker mutations other than the ones whose complementation relationships are being studied. In this way direct evidence for noncomplementation as well as for complementation can be obtained. Diploid colonies tend to produce sectors showing segregation of originally heterozygous markers; this is due both to occasional haploidization and to mitotic crossing-over leading to homozygosis in diploid nuclei (Pontecorvo *et al.*, 1953). This instability, however, is not sufficiently great to interfere seriously with the study of the properties of a diploid.

Rather similar techniques for the isolation of diploids have been applied to several other filamentous fungi.[1] A different approach was necessary in the case of the maize smut fungus *Ustilago maydis*. Holliday (1961) succeeded in selecting diploid strains by placing pieces of maize tissue, infected with the parasitic dikaryotic phase of the fungus, on to agar medium. Only the yeastlike monokaryotic phase can grow *in vitro*, and since a dikaryon is apparently unable to resolve itself into its haploid components, only the rare diploid monokaryon resulting from the fusion of the two nuclei in a dikaryotic cell is able to grow out and colonize the agar medium.

In the fission yeast *Schizosaccharomyces pombe* meiosis normally occurs at the next nuclear divisions after conjugation and nuclear fusion. However, a mating mixture of haploid cells of opposite mating types does give a small proportion of persistent diploids, and the colonies to which these give rise can be picked out visually because of the presence within them of ascospores (Leupold, 1955).

Another method of complementation testing in *Schizosaccharomyces* is described by Megnet and Giles (1964) in connection with their study of mutants deficient in the enzyme adenylosuccinase and requiring adenine for growth. Ascospores from a cross between the two mutants to be tested were spread on minimal agar medium containing eosin. A small number of prototrophic haploid recombinants generally grew to form colonies which were not stained by the eosin and were therefore white. In addition, any *diploid* ascospores, containing two complete mutant genomes, also grew if the mutants were complementary. Diploid ascospores, presumably due to some failure in meiosis, were always present when large numbers were plated, and the colonies to which they gave rise were self-fertile and came to contain large numbers of ascospores which stained pink with the eosin. Thus the presence of pink prototrophic colonies indicated complementation between the two mutants concerned.

1-4 COMPLEMENTATION TESTS IN BACTERIA

Stable heterokaryons and complete diploids which can propagate themselves as such are unknown in bacteria. Nevertheless, complementation tests can be carried out using partial diploids which can be obtained in a variety of ways. Fuller accounts of the bacterial genetic systems to be outlined briefly in the following paragraphs

[1] For diploids in *Coprinus* see Casselton (1965).

can be found in the excellent books by Jacob and Wollman (1961) and Hayes (1964).

Merozygotes in _Escherichia coli._ The _E. coli_ genome consists, at least in vegetatively multiplying cells, of a single closed loop of DNA, or "circular chromosome" (Cairns, 1963). In the well-known type of cross between F⁻ (recipient) and Hfr (high frequency recombination donor) strains the Hfr cells, each of which has an F (fertility) factor attached to its chromosome, tend to transfer a portion of their genomes to their F⁻ partners during conjugation. The particular segment which is transferred depends on the Hfr strain. Each independently isolated Hfr colony tends to have the F factor integrated at a different position on the chromosome, and it is at this point that the closed loop opens prior to genetic transfer. One side of the break becomes the chromosome "origin" and leads the way into the recipient cell. The other side becomes the trailing end of the entering chromosome, and remains attached to the F factor. The transfer is usually discontinued, apparently through breakage of the entering genetic strand, after only a part, seldom more than about a third, of the Hfr genome has entered the F⁻ cell. By using an appropriate Hfr strain, able to transfer the chromosome segment required, and by having an excess of Hfr over F⁻ cells in the mating mixture, it is possible to introduce a specific extra piece of genetic material into a high proportion of the F⁻ population. The immediate product of mating is called a _merozygote,_ meaning an incomplete zygote, because it is diploid only for part of the genome, being haploid for the remainder.

Although Lederberg (1949) showed that such partial diploidy can persist, at least in some strains, for a considerable number of generations, the merozygous condition is more usually a very unstable one. At every cell division following conjugation, recombination and segregation of the two homologous chromosome segments tend to occur with high probability (Anderson, 1958; Lederberg, 1957). Consequently merozygotes can be relied upon to give information on complementation between the two segments only during the restricted period between the entry of the Hfr segment and the first subsequent division of the F⁻ cell. Even then complementation can only be studied in relation to those functions of the Hfr genome which can express themselves at once without replacement of the original F⁻ cytoplasm. Merozygotes have been very little used in studies on interallelic complementation, which forms the main theme of this book, but they have given important information on the different and complementary functions of structure-determining and regulatory genes involved in enzyme formation for lactose utilization (Pardee, Jacob, and Monod, 1959), arabinose utilization (Helling and Weinberg, 1963), and arginine synthesis (Maas *et al.*, 1964).

Partial diploidy through attachment of chromosome segments to episomes. Chromosome fragments in *E. coli* are not, in general, able to replicate themselves independently of the complete genome. However, there is a class of genetic elements which can replicate autonomously in *E. coli* and related members of the Enterobacteriaceae. Examples of these elements, which are known as *episomes*, are the genomes of various temperate bacteriophages, of which the best known is lambda (λ), and the F (fertility) factor of *E. coli*. Through becoming attached to such episomes, segments of chromosomal material can also acquire the capacity for autonomous replication.

The first example of an episome "picking up" a short segment of bacterial chromosome was provided by Morse, Lederberg, and Lederberg (1956), who showed that lambda phage was specifically capable of carrying (*transducing*) a closely linked group of *E. coli* genes (the *gal* segment), which controls galactose utilization, from one bacterial cell to another. It has subsequently been shown that the lambda genome (*prophage*) has a specific site of attachment to the *E. coli* chromosome very close to the *gal* region. When the virus, either spontaneously or following induction with ultraviolet light, enters its phase of free multiplication and lyses the host cell, a small proportion of the lambda particles released are defective. They cannot carry out another cycle of infection with the production of a further generation of infective particles, although they can introduce their DNA into bacterial cells. Many of these defective phage particles appear to carry a portion of the bacterial chromosome, including much or all of the *gal* segment, in place of part of the regular phage genome. Bacteria which are infected by such particles become, in effect, diploid for some or all of the *gal* region. By growing lambda on a bacterial strain carrying one mutation in *gal*, and using the phage so obtained to infect cells carrying a second *gal* mutation, clones of cells carrying two *gal* segments with two different mutations are readily obtained. Such partial heterozygotes (*heterogenotes*) are not completely stable, since they segregate haploids of both parental and all possible recombinant types, but they are stable enough for their growth and enzymic properties to be investigated.

Although lambda is useful for studying complementation only within the *gal* region (Morse, 1959), other phages of a very similar kind are specific for other short segments of the *E. coli* genome. For example, phage ϕ80 (Matsushiro, Sato, and Kida, 1964) has a prophage attachment site very close to the *tryp* region. This is very fortunate, since it greatly facilitates genetic mapping and complementation studies of the two genes controlling the structure of tryptophan synthetase (Yanofsky, 1960; Yanofsky *et al.*, 1964).

More generally useful, since they are not restricted to any special region of the genome, are the F (fertility) factors. In an Hfr strain the F factor is attached to some specific chromosome site, but this may be a different site in different Hfr strains. In F⁺ (low fertility male) strains the F factor is present as a separate DNA fragment dividing autonomously and capable of being transferred rapidly from cell to cell by contact.

In Hfr cells the position of integration of the F factor defines the point at which the closed loop of the vegetative *E. coli* genome opens preparatory to transfer to an F⁻ conjugant. The F factor itself is usually attached to the extreme trailing end of the linear chromosome as it is injected; it only rarely enters the F⁻ cell and even then usually only after some two hours of conjugation. Consequently if one interrupts conjugation by mechanical agitation after short times, and selects for recombinants carrying a genetic marker from close to the trailing end of the Hfr chromosome (i.e., close to the integrated F factor) one expects a negative result. Such an experiment does, however, sometimes yield some recombinants of the type sought, and these behave as if they have received an autonomous F factor *carrying with it* a piece of bacterial chromosome including the selected marker. Evidently in such cases F has been "broken out" of the chromosome together with an adjacent piece of genetic material which has thus been enabled to enter the F⁻ cell unusually early. This sort of augmented F factor is known as an F-prime (F′), and it behaves like an ordinary F in its ability to be transmitted from cell to cell during only brief periods of conjugation. Thus having isolated a strain carrying a particular sort of F′ factor, one can introduce the factor, with its accompanying fragment of bacterial DNA, into any other *E. coli* strain of F⁻ mating type. By selecting for F′ factors from different Hfr strains with F integrated at different points it is possible to obtain almost any piece of the *E. coli* genome in the form of an autonomously replicating fragment. F′ factors certainly provide the most generally applicable method for making *E. coli* cells heterozygous for particular chromosome segments. The method has been used extensively for complementation analysis of the *lac* region (Jacob and Monod, 1961a) and of the *p* (alkaline phosphatase) gene (Garen and Echols, 1962; Garen and Garen, 1963). Like heterogenotes obtained by the use of lambda, F′ strains are not completely stable, but are stable enough for practical purposes.

Complementation tests in *Salmonella* by abortive transduction. When bacteriophage PLT22 (P22) is grown on one strain of *Salmonella typhimurium* (the donor strain) and used to infect another (recipient) strain, a proportion of the virus particles carry small fragments of donor genetic material, which can be derived from any part of the bacterial genome, into the recipient cells. In those cases where the recipient is not lysed by virulent growth of the phage, the donor segment can exhibit two kinds of behavior. It can become integrated, through some kind of recombinational event, into the recipient chromosome, and thus possibly bring about a change in the recipient genotype which is stably transmitted to all progeny cells. This is called *complete transduction*. Alternatively the donor segment may fail to become integrated, in which case it persists in the cell as a nonreplicating fragment. This latter case is called *abortive transduction* since, although the donor fragment may change the character of the immediate recipient, it cannot be transmitted to a clone of progeny cells. There are two situations in *Salmonella* in which abortive transduction can be readily detected. When the recipient strain is a nonmotile (nonflagellated) mutant and the donor strain is motile, or nonmotile for a different genetic reason, an abortive transduction with respect to motility shows up as a single cell which can move through soft agar medium leaving a trail of nonmotile progeny behind it (Stocker, 1956). Second, where the recipient strain is auxotrophic and the donor prototrophic, or auxotrophic because of mutation at a different complementary site, abortive transduction results in a single prototrophic cell. This cell can continue dividing on minimal medium, but from each division only one of the two daughter cells receives the transducing fragment and hence the potential for further division. The result is a colony increasing in size by increments of one cell at a time or, if the auxotrophic cells are able to divide a few more times before exhausting their nutritional reserves, of a few cells at a time. Thus abortive transduction gives colonies which are very minute compared with the exponentially growing colonies resulting from complete transduction (Ozeki, 1956) (Figure 1-3). Such minute colonies formed on minimal medium can be easily seen under relatively low magnification, and provide evidence that the donor strain can provide a genetic fragment which can compensate for the defect in the re-

FIGURE 1-3   *Salmonella typhimurium* colonies due to complete and abortive transduction. Phage grown on one histidine-requiring mutant was used to infect a second complementary histidine-requiring mutant, and transduced prototrophic survivors were selected on minimal agar medium. The arrows indicate microcolonies due to abortive transduction; the large colonies are due to complete transduction. Enlarged $\times$ 27. From Hartman, Hartman, and Serman (1960).

cipient genome. In other words, abortive transduction is evidence for complementation and the absence of abortive transduction is evidence that the donor and recipient strains are mutant with respect to noncomplementary segments of genetic material. Complementation tests by this method have been carried out most extensively by Hartman and his colleagues in their analysis of *Salmonella* histidine-requiring mutants (Hartman, Hartman, and Serman, 1960).

Though abortive transduction provides a sensitive qualitative test for the presence or absence of complementation, it is not suitable for quantitative estimates of the degree of complementation in any particular case or for studies on the nature of the complementation product. Only a very small fraction of the survivors of a population treated with transducing phage will be abortively transduced with respect to any particular gene, and there is no way of obtaining a specific kind of abortive transductant in bulk.

1-5   COMPLEMENTATION IN BACTERIOPHAGES

So far, complementation analysis in bacteriophages has been practically confined to the *E. coli* phages T2 and T4,[2] but the principles involved should apply to phages in general. Different bacteriophage genomes can easily be introduced into the same bacterial cell by mixed infection. Particles of two phage strains are added to a suspension of bacteria in sufficient excess to insure that most of the bacteria will be infected by at least one particle of each kind. When two individually defective phage genomes are present in the same host cell each is able to benefit from the functions provided by the other provided that the two mutations are in complementary genetic segments. Different kinds of test can be made, depending on the nature of the defect in the phage strains concerned.

The classical complementation analysis in bacteriophage was made by Benzer (1955, 1958) of the *r* (rapid lysis) mutants of phage T4. These mutants are characterized by the formation of extra-large plaques when plated on a lawn of cells of strain B of *E. coli*. The *r* mutants fell into three quite distinct classes on the basis of their growth on other *E. coli* strains, and the *rII* class were distinguished by their inability to form plaques on any strain, such as K12 (λ), harboring lambda prophage. Within *rII* there turned out to be two subclasses A and B. When a K12 (λ) cell was infected with a mixture of *rIIA* and *rIIB* phage particles it was lysed, with the release of a full yield of virus particles, but mixed infection with two *rIIA* or two *rIIB* mutants never led to lysis (but see footnote on p. 28). The two kinds of *rII* mutation are localized in two adjacent but nonoverlapping segments of the T4 genome, and these two segments are evidently complementary in function. Complementation testing of *rII* mutants can be carried out very rapidly by superimposing drops of suspensions of different mutant phages onto a lawn of cells of K12 (λ). Lysis, leading to a circular clearing in the region of a mixed inoculum, indicates complementation.

A very similar kind of rapid test was applied by Edgar, Denhardt, and Epstein (1964) to the large and heterogeneous class of temperature-sensitive (*ts*) mutants of T4 (cf. Chapter 5). These mutants cannot grow at all at 42°C, but are more or less normal at 25°C. For qualitative complementation tests, overlapping spots of different mutants were placed on a plate heavily seeded with bacteria, and the plate was then incubated at 42°C. The individual mutants were un

---

[2] But see Tessmann (1965) for complementation tests with phage S13.

able to grow; complementation was shown by a clearing where two spots overlapped. The test was made quantitative by measuring the *yield* of phage (burst size) from mixed infected bacteria. Cells were infected with an average of four phage particles of each of two mutant types, unadsorbed phage was neutralized with antiserum, and the suspension was diluted and incubated at 39.5°C. After a fixed time (30 or 60 minutes), the cells were lysed artificially by the addition of chloroform and the number of phage particles in the lysate was measured by plaque formation at 25°C. Different pairs of mutants gave very different degrees of complementation, the yields of phage ranging from close to the usual wild-type number down to little more than would have been given by the mutants individually. These results are discussed in detail in Chapter 5.

A rather different problem is presented by mutants with restricted host range whose defect consists in being unable to *infect* a particular bacterial strain. Host range depends in large measure on the nature of the bacteriophage tail fibers through which attachment is made to the bacterial cell surface. During a mixed infection the protein components for the assembly of the completed phage particles are drawn from a common pool, and tail fiber protein molecules made under the control of different phage genomes may be incorporated into the same bacteriophage. If the mutant protein components can complement each other, some of the viruses released from a mixedly infected cell will be able to infect the bacterial strain immune to the individual mutants. Thus the test would be to make a mixed infection of a strain susceptible to infection by the original restricted mutants, and then to test the phage progeny to see whether their host range was now de-restricted. It should be noted that what is observed in this test is the consequence of the mixture of genomes in the *previous* cycle of infection rather than of the genotypes of the particles showing the complementary effect.

1-6 CONCLUSION

The essence of all the kinds of tests which have been described is to determine whether two different, though homologous, pieces of genetic material present in the same cytoplasm can support functions which neither could support by itself. Several fundamental differences between the various systems should, however, be noted. First, in fungi and other organisms possessing a nuclear membrane, there is a distinction between diploid heterozygotes, in which different homologous genomes are present within the same nucleus, and haploid heterokaryons, where they are present in a common cytoplasm but in different nuclei. Second, there is the distinction between those cases where two *complete* genomes coexist, as in diploids, heterokaryons, and mixed phage infections, and those where only a fragment of one genome is added to a complete homologous genome, as in all the bacterial systems. Third, there is the important difference between those systems where the two genetic homologues can replicate and remain together through an indefinite number of cell divisions (heterokaryons, diploids, and bacterial heterogenotes) and those in which the complementation situation is confined to the one cell in which it arose (bacterial merozygotes and abortive transductants). A mixed bacteriophage infection is clearly in a category of its own from this point of view. Finally, there are those systems in which the ratio of the homologous pieces of genetic material can vary within quite wide limits, as in heterokaryons and mixed phage infections, and those others in which it is strictly one-to-one.

In spite of this wide diversity, it seems that all these systems give equivalent information, at least at the qualitative level. Exceptions to this rule, for example, positive complementation in a fungal diploid with a negative result in the corresponding heterokaryon (cf. Pontecorvo, 1963), should be carefully looked for, but no clear and well-documented examples of such exceptions seem to exist at present.

2

FROM THE GENE TO THE CISTRON

The concept of the gene arose directly from the factorial mode of inheritance first clearly demonstrated in peas by Mendel in 1865, and established as the general rule in both plants and animals by a number of different workers nearly 40 years later. The word gene was proposed by Johannsen in 1907 and was given wide currency by Morgan (1919) following the definitive work on *Drosophila melanogaster* by Morgan *et al.* (1915).

2-1 THE TWO DEFINITIONS OF THE GENE

It seemed clear to the pioneers of Mendelian genetics that the gene was an indivisible unit of genetic transmission. The firm establishment of the chromosome theory, and the demonstration that the number of genes in *Drosophila* far outnumbered the chromosomes, led to the view of the gene as "a certain amount of material in the chromosome that may separate from the chromosome in which it lies and be replaced by a corresponding part (and none other) of the homologous chromosome" (Morgan, 1919). Thus a gene could be separated from neighboring genes by crossing-over, but crossing-over was not supposed ever to occur within a gene. This kind of definition says nothing about whether one gene has one biochemical function or several.

However, another generalization about genes soon became possi-

19

ble, mainly as a result of the study of *multiple allelic series,* that is, of series of genes which appeared to be alternative occupants of the same chromosomal locus. Such series nearly always seemed to cause different degrees of modification of the same trait in the organism. A famous example in *Drosophila* is the series of eye colors controlled by alleles at the sex-linked *w* locus. All of these—the red-brown wild-type color *(w⁺)*, *white (w)*, *apricot (wᵃ)*, *eosin (wᵉ)*, *cherry (wᶜʰ)*, and several others—could be reasonably considered as representing different degrees of quantitative impairment of the same process, namely, some step in eye pigment synthesis. More important than their superficial resemblance, however, was the fact that they failed to show complementation in heterozygous females (males, of course, cannot be heterozygous for the X chromosome). The heterozygotes w^+/w and w^+/w^a, obtained as the female progeny of wild × *white* and wild × *apricot* crosses, both had eyes of normal color, showing that neither *w* nor w^a actually inhibited eye pigment synthesis when a functional w^+ gene was present. The w/w^a heterozygotes, from a *white* × *apricot* cross, had pale apricot eyes, as if *w* and w^a were acting more or less additively without complementation. This is strong evidence that *white* and *apricot* are defective in the same metabolic process. The same sort of noncomplementary relationship held between all other pairs within the series. Noncomplementation turned out to be the almost universal rule in multiple allelic series.

This type of result stood in marked contrast to what was found when eye color mutants controlled by different chromosome loci were crossed together. For example, the female F_1 progeny from a cross between *white* (X chromosome) and *scarlet* (*st*—third chromosome) had eyes of wild-type color; in other words, the two mutants showed complementation. This is a thoroughly reasonable result, since the *white* parent would have contributed a third chromosome carrying st^+ while the scarlet parent would have contributed an X chromosome carrying w^+ to each of the female progeny, which would thus be of constitution $w/w^+ \ st/st^+$, with both wild-type genes present and functional. The same kind of complementation test showed the functional distinctness of genes at different loci on the same chromosome. Thus *brown* (*bw*—lacking the red component of the normal eye color) and cinnabar (*cn*—lacking the normal brown component) are both located on the second chromosome, though showing some 40% recombination at meiosis. The double heterozygote from the *brown* × *cinnabar* cross, represented as $\dfrac{cn^+ \ bw}{cn \ bw^+}$, has eyes of wild-type color, confirming that the two mutants are defective in different processes of eye pigment synthesis.

The general success of the rule that genes at different loci show complementation, while different alleles at a single locus (i.e., alleles of a single gene) do not, led to the more or less tacit acceptance of the diploid complementation test as a means of defining the gene. Thus there arose two alternative definitions of the gene—as an indivisible unit of transmission, and as a unit of function defined by complementation tests. These two definitions coexisted with very little conflict from the time of the early *Drosophila* work until about 1950. The occasional anomalies which arose during this time mostly took the form of complementation between supposedly allelic genes.

For example, in maize (*Zea mays*), two chromosome "loci" concerned with pigmentation both showed complementary action of supposed alleles. At the R locus, four of the many known "alleles" were designated R^r, R^g, r^r and r^g respectively. R^r gave anthocyanin pigmentation both in the aleurone layer of the seed and in the vegetative parts of the plant, R^g gave pigment in the seed only, r^r in the plant only, and r^g in neither. In all pairwise combinations of these four, the presence of pigment in a given tissue was dominant over its absence, and the compound R^g/r^r showed pigment in both seed and plant. Thus r^r and R^g were complementary, as if seed and plant pigmentation represented different genetic functions (Stadler and Fogel, 1945; Stadler, 1946).

A somewhat similar situation at the A locus of maize was investigated by Laughnan (1948). Here one allele, A^b, determined both purple anthocyanin pigmentation in the plant and in the endosperm of the seed and a brown pigment, formed to the exclusion of anthocyanin, in the pericarp. Among the other alleles, some, generally designated A, determined anthocyanin in plant, endosperm, *and* pericarp (with no brown pigment), while others, exemplified by A^d, resembled A^b in determining dominant brown pericarp pigmentation but promoted very little anthocyanin formation in the plant and endosperm. The compound A/A^d gave almost the same phenotype as A^b, A contributing the purple plant color and A^d the brown pericarp color. Though the biosynthetic relationships of the two pigments were (and remain) obscure, it seemed reasonable to suggest that A^b comprised two distinct functional units, one concerned with plant and one with pericarp color.

Laughnan (1949, 1952) was, in fact, able to recover an A^d-like component apparently free of the plant color determinant by crossing-over between A^b and an allele a possessing neither function. Later a good case was made for the physical divisibility of the R locus into two functionally distinct genes, the separation in this case apparently depending on unequal crossing over (Stadler and Emmerling, 1956). Thus these two examples from maize did not involve any. contradiction between the two alternative definitions of the gene, but rather served as a vindication of the ability of the complementation criterion to resolve different genes in cases where recombinational analysis had not at first been sensitive enough to do so.[1]

The development of *Neurospora crassa* as a genetic organism, and especially the discovery and exploitation of auxotrophic mutants by Beadle and Tatum (1945), brought an increased emphasis on the complementation test for allelism. Hundreds of auxotrophs of *Neurospora* were assigned to loci, that is, to different allelomorphic series, mainly on the basis of their complementation relationships in heterokaryons, which were much quicker to make and score than were sexual crosses.[2] The justification for this procedure was that, where sexual crossing analysis was also carried out, pairs of noncomplementary auxotrophs were almost never found to give prototrophic recombinants in samples of hundreds or thousands of ascospores; such numbers were, at the time of the early *Neurospora* work, considered reasonably large.

2-2 THE *CIS-TRANS* POSITION EFFECT IN *DROSOPHILA*

At the same time as the *Neurospora* workers were placing great emphasis on functional allelism, as defined by complementation tests with heterokaryons, the first cracks were beginning to appear in the concept of the functional gene as an indivisible unit. Lewis, in 1945, showed that recombination was demonstrable between two *Drosophila* mutants which were functionally allelic. One of these mutants, *Star* (*S*), was lethal in the homozygous condition and in the heterozygote (*S/S⁺*) caused a slight reduction in the size of the eye and a roughening of its surface texture. The other was a recessive, subsequently called *asteroid* (*ast*), which caused, when homozygous, an extreme reduction in the size of the eye with the same sort of roughness as in S/S^+. The compound *S/ast* gave an even more extreme reduction in eye size; the mutants showed no complementation. Lewis showed that *S/ast* hetrozygotes showed a low frequency (0.02%) of recombinant gametes of two kinds, those carrying *both* mutations (*S ast*) and those carrying neither (*S⁺ ast⁺*). The separability of the sites of the two mutations was thus proved.

[1] The cases of complementary action of functionally somewhat distinct "alleles" recorded by Whiting (1951) in parasitic wasps belonging to the genera *Habrobracon* and *Mormoniella* could well be of the same kind.

[2] For a particularly good example of the value of complementation tests for distinguishing closely linked and superficially similar genes in *Neurospora* see De Serres (1956).

The occurrence of these recombinants made it possible to compare the two kinds of double heterozygote, the *cis* arrangement, $\dfrac{S \; ast}{S^+ \; ast^+}$ and the *trans*, $\dfrac{S \; ast^+}{S^+ \; ast}$. The two were strikingly different in phenotype (Figure 2-1). The latter, as already stated, gave a very much reduced eye; the former, with one *completely* wild-type chromosome segment opposite a doubly mutant one, had an eye only slightly smaller than normal, much like that given by S alone. This is an example of a *cis-trans* position effect. In the *cis* configuration the wild-type elements are linked in the same chromosome and show complementary action in the development of a normal phenotype, while in the *trans* arrangement they are separated in different homologous chromosomes and fail to complement.

FIGURE 2-1   A *cis-trans* position effect in *Drosophila melanogaster*. On the bottom: $S \; ast/S^+ \; ast^+$. On the top: $S \; ast^+/S^+ \; ast$ (see text). From E. B. Lewis (1951).

Subsequently a number of other examples were found in *Drosophila* of mutants mapping at closely linked but separables sites and showing the *cis-trans* position effect. For example, Lewis (1952) and Green (1959) showed that the classical *w* series of alleles could be subdivided into at least three groups, mapping at very close but distinct sites. The standard *white* allele *w* mapped at one site, *apricot* (w^a) at another, and *cherry* (w^{ch}) and *eosin* (w^e) at yet a third. These mutants show the *cis-trans* position effect in every pairwise combination. Thus while, as mentioned above, females of constitution $\dfrac{w\ \ +}{+\ \ w^a}$ have pale apricot eyes, those of constitution $\dfrac{w\ \ w^a}{+\ \ +}$ had the normal wild-type pigmentation.

The *Drosophila* workers referred to the relationship between mutants which were functionally noncomplementary and yet mapped at different sites as *pseudoallelism*. In fact, it turned out that there was at least some pseudoallelism within practically every one of the classical multiple allelic series of *Drosophila* in which it was looked for. The work of the Greens (Green and Green, 1949, 1956; Green, 1961a) on the *lozenge* locus is a particularly good example; several others are cited in an excellent review by Carlson (1959a).

Two interpretations of pseudoalleles were possible. The first, favored by Lewis (1955) and Green (1963), was that each separable element of a locus showing pseudoallelism was really a distinct gene with a distinct function. On this view the *cis-trans* effect was explained on the basis that the functions of pseudoallelic genes might be related in such a way that the product of the activity of one gene was the substrate for the activity of the adjacent one. If the product was very unstable, or produced in a very small amount, it might be capable of being handed on to the adjacent gene on the same chromosome while not being able to survive the passage from one chromosome to its homologue. This might be termed the "bucket brigade" hypothesis. It amounts to maintaining that the recombinational unit is equivalent to the functional unit, while denying that a negative complementation test provides adequate evidence for functional identity.

There are several objections to this hypothesis. In the first place it postulates a rather special mode of gene interaction for which there is no other evidence (though, as we shall see, certain kinds of "operon" situation might give the same effect). Perhaps more important, if it were true one would expect that the "loci" showing pseudoallelism should not be indefinitely subdivisible but should each consist of a finite and reasonably small number of genes. Some *Dro-*

sophila workers, particularly Green (1955, 1959, 1963) have argued strongly that this is indeed the case. It is certainly true that within a given pseudoallelic series the number of identified recombinable sites is usually considerably less than the number of mutants.[3] To take the examples reviewed by Carlson (1959a), two sites have been identified among five mutants in the *S-ast* series, two among three mutants in *stubble,* three among 18 in *lozenge,* two among three in *vermilion,* two among eleven in *forked,* three among six in *singed,* three among four in *garnet,* and four among over 30 in *white.* However, it is far from clear that the apparent limit to the subdivisibility of these loci was not a consequence of the comparatively limited numbers of progeny which one can score from *Drosophila* crosses. Even the distinctions between pseudoallelic sites which have been made have generally depended on the finding of fewer than ten recombinant flies in a progeny of the order of 10^4 or 10^5 individuals, which is about as many as it is practicable to score. A recombination frequency of the order of 10^{-5}, though commonplace in fungal or bacterial genetics, would very probably not be detected in a *Drosophila* experiment. If one bears in mind the limits of the resolving power of the analysis, the available data on *Drosophila* pseudo-alleles do not argue in favor of a small and limited number of genes for each "locus" but seem quite consistent with *Drosophila* loci in general being quite finely subdivisible by crossing over.

The second interpretation of pseudoalleles is that they represent mutations at different and separable sites within a single gene. On this view the gene can only function when all its parts are assembled together in one unit, and its function can be impaired by mutation at any one of numerous separable points along its length. This amounts to saying that the gene, as a unit of function, is *not* an indivisible unit, but only appeared to be so because of the inadequate resolving power of the recombinational analysis, and that a negative complementation test *is* good evidence for functional identity. This seems a perfectly adequate hypothesis, and one which is in line with the well-established concepts of microbial genetics, to be reviewed later. It is, however, necessary to be clear about what one means by

---

[3] However, Welshons and von Halle (1962) found that ten mutants at the *notch* locus were all at different sites. More recently Chovnick, *et al.* (1964) have, through an ingenious automatic selective technique, obtained a twentyfold increase in the resolving power of recombinational analysis in *Drosophila,* and have demonstrated at the *rosy* locus a situation approximating to the microbial norm, with some separable sites showing recombination frequencies of the order of 10^{-5}–10^{-6}.

functional identity. Two pseudoallelic mutants may, and indeed usually do, look somewhat different. This could be explained by saying that *different* primary biochemical functions are affected in the two mutants, or that the *same* function is affected in different ways or to different extents. As Green (1963) has stressed, mere visual inspection of a complex morphological phenotype cannot distinguish these two possibilities. The complementation criterion, if one is content to interpret it in the simple and obvious way, *does* distinguish them in the sense that noncomplementation indicates one function. It remains true that so far in *Drosophila* it has been possible to validate the complementation criterion by direct investigation of the primary biochemical action of genes in only a very few cases (e.g., Glassman, 1962; Glassman and Pinkerton, 1960; Schalet, Kernaghan, and Chovnick, 1964). In microorganisms such investigation is often possible and places the interpretation of complementation tests on a much firmer basis.

It is only fair to point out that, though one may reject a "bucket brigade" type of hypothesis as a *general* explanation for pseudoallelism, the central idea of this hypothesis, that some interactions between genes may depend on their being on the same chromosome rather than on homologous chromosomes, has subsequently been vindicated, though in a different theoretical context. This point is discussed and further elaborated in the section on operons in the next chapter.

2-3   FINE STRUCTURE OF GENES IN MICROORGANISMS AND VIRUSES

Whatever the situation in *Drosophila,* there is no doubt that in fungi, bacteria, and viruses it is the exception rather than the rule for two independently isolated noncomplementary mutants to occupy exactly the same genetic site.

In *Neurospora crassa* early indications of the recombinational complexity of functionally single genes were reported by Bonner (1950) and, in more detail, by Giles (1951). However, the first major advance in the understanding of genetic fine structure of fungi came with the pioneering work on *Aspergillus nidulans* by Pontecorvo and Roper.

At the outset of the investigation these workers were influenced by the "bucket brigade" concept, particularly as it might apply to the biosynthesis of compounds such as vitamins which might be formed only in very small amounts (Pontecorvo, 1950). With this in mind Roper (1950) looked for linkage between mutations causing a requirement for biotin, and, in fact, found that three such mutations were at three extremely closely linked though separable chromosomal sites. Further investigation, however, failed to show any physiological distinction between the three mutants, all of which showed growth responses to the same set of biotin precursors. Even more significantly, they proved to be noncomplementary in diploids and heterokaryons (Roper, in Pontecorvo *et al.*, 1953). Somewhat later Pritchard (1955) showed that four noncomplementary adenine-requiring mutants of *Aspergillus* were all at distinct though closely linked genetic sites. In this case a *cis-trans* position effect of the *Drosophila* type was formally demonstrated (Roper and Pritchard, 1955). Through special techniques the two doubly heterozygous diploid strains $\frac{ad16\ ad8}{+\quad +}$ and $\frac{ad16\ +}{+\ ad8}$ were synthesized. The first, the *cis* heterozygote, was adenine-independent, while the second, the *trans* heterozygote, was adenine-requiring. The main difference from the *Drosophila* situation was that no mutant was found which could be a "true" allele of any other—all were at different sites.

At the same time as these important results were being obtained in *Aspergillus*, Benzer (1955, 1958) was establishing the same kind of situation in much greater detail in T4 bacteriophage. The characteristics of the *rII* mutants of T4 have been described in the preceding chapter. Benzer found that the great majority of pairs of *rII* mutants would, when made to multiply together in the same bacterial cells, give a low frequency of wild-type recombinants among the progeny phage particles. This showed that the number of independently mutable and separable sites within the *rII* genetic region must be large. Indeed, a total of over 2400 *rII* mutants have been assigned to 308 different sites, and the number of sites which are so far represented by only one mutant suggests that there are *at least* 120 other sites remaining to be discovered. Benzer was able to place each mutant in one of a linear series of genetic segments defined by reference to a standard series of overlapping deletion mutants. For details of the method the reader is referred to Benzer's papers (1958, 1961). Within each segment the order of the sites could be established through quantitative estimates of recombination frequencies. The result is a picture of the *rII* region as a linear structure consisting of at least 400 individually mutable and recombinable elements.

From the amount of genetic recombination between the ends of the *rII* region (about 10%), the best estimate of the total genetic length of the T4 genome (about 2500 recombination units according to Stahl, Edgar, and Steinberg, 1964), and the total amount of DNA per T4 particle (equivalent to about 2×10^5 nucleotide pairs) it is possible to make a rough estimate of the amount of DNA in the *rII* region. On this basis it seems that there are probably of the order of a thousand nucleotide pairs composing the *rII* segment, a number which is not large compared with the number of identifiable genetic sites.

Although the *rII* region was a continuum so far as recombination was concerned it could be subdivided cleanly into two functionally distinct segments *A* and *B*, which were contiguous but not over-lapping. Any mutant in *A* was complementary in mixed infection with any mutant in *B*, but no complementation was found between any two *A* or any two *B* mutants.[4] Thus the complementation test here reveals a clear segmentation into functional units, whereas re-combinational analysis shows no unit larger than something of the order of size of a nucleotide pair.

The pattern of very fine divisibility, first established for a few genetic regions in *Aspergillus* and bacteriophage (and also in *Salmonella*, see Demerec *et al.*, 1955), was soon shown to be universal in microorganisms. It is not necessary to review the numerous cases in which many mutants, all superficially similar in phenotype and noncomplementary in at any rate most pairwise combinations, have been shown to be due to mutation at many different sites within a short chromosome segment. Dozens of examples are known in *Aspergillus*, *Neurospora*, yeast (both *Saccharomyces* and *Schizosaccharomyces*), *Escherichia coli*, *Salmonella typhimurium*, and T4 bacteriophage, to name only the more popular genetic objects. Demerec and Hartman's review covers the examples known up to 1959.

These findings pose a problem in genetic nomenclature. Pseudo-allelism turned out to be so much more the rule than the exception in microorganisms that the use of the term, with its implication of a *special* relationship between mutants, was virtually abandoned ex-cept by some *Drosophila* geneticists. The concept of the gene was left in a state of some confusion.

Benzer (1958) proposed a set of new definitions which took ac-

---

[4] Later work (Champe and Benzer, personal communication) revealed some degree of complementation between some pairs of *rIIA* mutants. The results with these mutants could be represented by a complementation map in the form of a closed loop or, if one result was omitted, a straight line. This further complication does not, however, obscure the very clear distinction between *A* and *B* mutants. See Table 3-2.

count of the new analyses of genetic fine structure in microorganisms. The *muton* was defined as the smallest element which could mutate independently of neighboring elements to produce an observable effect in the phenotype, and the *recon* as the smallest element which could be separated by genetic recombination. Subsequent work has failed to show any distinction between these units. It is, indeed, difficult to think of any operation by means of which two mutons could be shown to fall within one recon, since the distinction between mutant sites depends on their being separable by recombination. Everything points to mutons and recons being equivalent and corresponding, at least in microorganisms, to single DNA nucleotide pairs.

It was Benzer's third coinage which has been the most influential. He observed that "a group of non-complementary mutants falls within a limited segment of the genetic map," and proposed that "such a map segment, corresponding to a function which is unitary as defined by the *cis-trans* test" should be referred to as a *cistron*. Thus the term cistron included all those well-known loci in *Drosophila* whose status had been made uncertain by the discovery of pseudoallelism, as well as many loci in microorganisms which were fairly clearly units of biochemical function in spite of being finely subdivisible by recombination. The word filled a real need and was widely adopted.

Table 2-1 shows the *cis-trans* test applied in its full rigor to the definition of cistrons in the *rII* region of bacteriophage T4. In practice, however, cistrons have more usually been recognized without carrying out the full *cis-trans* comparison. The rigorous test involves comparing the *trans* heterozygote $m' +/+ m''$ (where m' and m'' are two different mutant sites) with the *cis* double heterozygote $m' m''/+ +$. The synthesis of the latter depends on the isolation of a double mutant strand, which is usually impossible to select for and in any case difficult to recognize where the single mutants have similar rather extreme effects. Where both single mutants are recessive to wild type and both show a more or less complete functional deficiency, the double mutant can be expected to be recessive also. In other words the *cis* compound $m' m''/+ +$ may in general be expected to be functionally normal. This expectation has been borne out in those few cases where the double mutant strand has been obtained and tested. Consequently it is usual, at least with mutants which individually have fairly extreme but recessive deficiencies, to take the normal phenotype of the *cis* compound for granted and to look only at the readily obtained *trans* combination. Thus the *cis-trans* test tends to be replaced by a simple complementation test,

TABLE 2-1 *cis-trans* Comparisons with Various *rII* Mutants of Bacteriophage T4 [*], [†]

	Infecting phage	Burst size
	Wild only	250
cis	*r147 r205* + Wild	245
trans	*r147* + *r205*	0.00
cis	*r360 r287* + Wild	338
trans	*r360* + *r287*	0.00
cis	*r147 r360* + Wild	306
trans	*r147* + *r360*	290
cis	*r147 r287* + Wild	216
trans	*r147* + *r287*	264
cis	*r205 r360* + Wild	264
trans	*r205* + *r360*	261
cis	*r205 r287* + Wild	263
trans	*r205* + *r287*	250

[*] On the basis of these and other tests, *r147* and *r205* are assigned to the A cistron and *r287* and *r360* to the B cistron.
[†] The table shows the average number of phage particles ("burst size") released from each K12 (λ) cell after infection with the indicated phage mixture under standard conditions. Data of Champe and Benzer (personally communicated by Dr. S. E. Champe).

the cistron becoming a region within which mutants do not complement each other.

2-4 THE FUNCTION OF THE CISTRON

Numerous cases are known in a variety of microorganisms in which the function of the cistron is evidently to determine the structure of a single enzyme (see review by Fincham, 1960). However, one very fully investigated example shows that "one cistron—one enzyme" is sometimes an oversimplification and that "one cistron—one polypeptide chain" is a more accurate formulation.

One large group of tryptophan-requiring mutants in *E. coli* lack normal tryptophan synthetase activity, and all are located within the same short genetic segment. This segment can, however, be divided into two adjacent cistrons (Yanofsky and Crawford, 1959). An extract of any mutant in cistron A will form tryptophan synthetase activity when mixed with an extract of any mutant of cistron B. The reason for this was shown by Crawford and Yanofsky (1958). *Escherichia coli* tryptophan synthetase is a complex of two quite distinct proteins. Mutants of class A are defective only in protein A, and mutants of class B defective only in protein B. In the mixed extracts the active enzyme is readily formed by combination of the two good components, one contributed by each mutant. The A protein certainly consists only of a single polypeptide chain, and the same may be true of the B component.

The function of the tryptophan synthetase A cistron has been worked out more thoroughly than that of any other cistron in any organism. Most of the amino acid sequence of the A polypeptide chain is now known, and the effects on this primary structure of some dozen different mutations have been established. Each mutant produces a type of polypeptide chain differing from the normal in just one amino acid. When the positions of the amino acid substitutions in the several mutants were compared with those of the corresponding mutant sites in the genetic map of the A cistron, the amino acid and genetic sequences were found to correspond perfectly. Even the relative spacing of the amino acid substitutions was closely similar to that of the corresponding genetic sites (Yanofsky *et al.*, 1964). Thus this cistron forms a linear code for the amino acid sequence of a specific polypeptide chain. It appears overwhelmingly likely that this case, though the only one so far worked out in such detail, can stand as a general model of cistron action.

2-5 GENETIC TERMINOLOGY

In spite of the widespread adoption of the term cistron, most geneticists have been loath to abandon the use of the older terms gene and allele. These words have the advantage of euphony, and, though they may have contained a more or less concealed ambiguity, their meaning in context has usually been clear. Geneticists have usually understood the gene to be something associated with a small segment of chromosome and having a specific function. The cistron appeared to many merely as a more precise way of defining the gene in which they had always believed. Accordingly, in much, and perhaps most, of the current genetical literature *gene* is now used in the same sense as *cistron*. The latter term has itself developed a certain ambiguity, as will become apparent in the next chapter.

In the remainder of this book *gene* is used as synonymous with *cistron,* and *allele* is used to mean one specific form of a cistron or gene. Two mutants described as *allelic* are considered to carry mutant forms of the same cistron.

In the literature relating to complementation *interallelic* (or simply *allelic*) means the same as *intracistronic* or *intragenic*, while *intercistronic* means the same as *intergenic*. *Interallelic* and *intergenic* are generally used in this book.

The term *locus* is more noncommittal and therefore often very useful. It is usually used to mean a short chromosome segment within which mutations of broadly similar phenotypic effect can occur, but it does not necessarily imply that the functional relationships of these mutations are understood.

3

EQUIVOCAL CISTRONS

Benzer's definition of the cistron brought about a great clarification in thinking about the nature of the gene, and it quickly became very widely accepted. Nevertheless, it was not long before facts which were inconsistent with Benzer's clear-cut concept began to force themselves on the attention of geneticists.

3-1 REDEFINING THE CISTRON

The kind of situation which came to light was the following. A number of mutants are isolated which all, superficially at least, have the same sort of phenotype, map in the same short genetic segment, and give negative complementation tests in all combinations. On these grounds they are attributed without hesitation to the same cistron or gene. However, as a larger number of mutants of the same general type are isolated a few pairwise combinations of them are found to show complementation, although many or most mutants of the series remain noncomplementary with all the rest. This, essentially, was what was found in *Neurospora crassa* by Fincham and Pateman (1957) for mutants at the *am* locus, by Giles, Partridge, and Nelson (1957) for the *ad-4* locus, and by Catcheside and Overton (1958) for several series of arginine- and histidine-requiring mutants. Numerous further examples in *Neurospora*, and several more in *Aspergillus* (cf. Pontecorvo, 1959), *Salmonella*, and

Escherichia coli followed. Limited complementation was even found among certain mutants of the classical *rIIA* cistron of bacteriophage T4, as is shown in Table 3-2. A formally very similar situation has been demonstrated in *Drosophila* both at the *rudimentary* locus (Fahmy and Fahmy, 1959) and at the *yellow* locus (Green, 1961b).

What are we to make of this sort of situation? At first sight such results might seem to invalidate the cistron as a meaningful unit. In the view of most microbial geneticists, however, it is still possible to recognize discrete units of genetic function. How does one define such units, and how do they relate to the cistron concept? In the following sections I will review some main criteria which one can use.

Functional overlapping of complementing by noncomplementing mutants. We saw earlier that in numerous cases where a short genetic segment, or locus, at first seemed to conform to the definition of a cistron, it was later found that some mutants were mutually complementary. It is characteristic of this sort of situation that, while there may be several classes of mutants which are complementary in all pairwise combinations, yet other mutants are noncomplementary with ("overlap") two or more of the complementary classes, and many mutants, often constituting an absolute majority, overlap all the rest. The complementation relationships of the whole series of mutants can be represented by a diagram, or *complementation map*, which is very often, though not invariably (see Chapter 5), linear in form. The principle on which a complementation map is constructed is that mutually complementing mutants are represented by nonoverlapping, and noncomplementing pairs by overlapping, lines, each line being continuous (see Figure 3-1). Good examples of complementation maps from *Neurospora* are provided by the loci *arg-1* (Figure 3-1), *ad-4* (Figure 3-2), and *pan-2* (Figure 3-3).

In recent years complementation maps have been popularized by *Neurospora* workers, but it may be pointed out that essentially the same device for representing the functional relationships of apparently allelic mutants was used by Dubinin and his group as long ago as 1930 (Dubinin, 1932a, 1933). The Russian workers made an intensive study of the *scute (sc)* series of mutants in *Drosophila melanogaster*. Each member of the *sc* series, when homozygous, eliminates certain bristles on the body of the fly, and two different mutant alleles may affect different, but often overlapping, sets of bristles. On the basis of the overlaps it was found to be possible to represent the functional relationships of the alleles in a linear diagram. Heterozygous flies carrying two different alleles were missing only those bristles which were affected by both alleles. This kind of complementary action is, however, only doubtfully comparable to the inter-

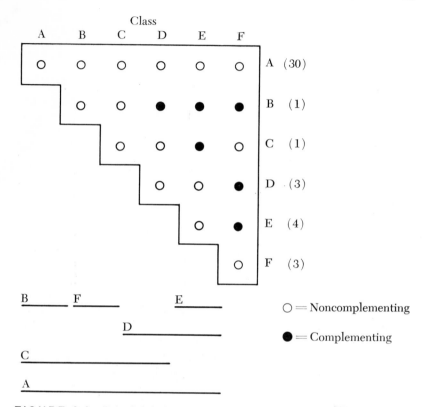

FIGURE 3-1   Principle of construction of a complementation map, as illustrated by mutants of the *arg-1* series in *Neurospora crassa*. Patterns of complementation of six classes of mutants (number in each class in parenthesis) are shown above. The representation of the results by a complementation map is shown below. The order of segments of B and F is arbitrary. From Catcheside and Overton (1958).

allelic complementation in microorganisms with which we are concerned here; its possible significance will be discussed in Chapter 4.

The finding of noncomplementary relationships which provide a continuous series of overlaps, linking the mutually complementary classes of mutants, makes it difficult to regard the genetic region in question as consisting of a number of discrete functional units. For such a hypothesis would imply that many or most mutants eliminate some or all of the functions simultaneously, and this would run contrary to the general experience that point mutations usually have very specific single biochemical effects. The simplest way of explaining the overlaps on a conventional basis would be to attribute them

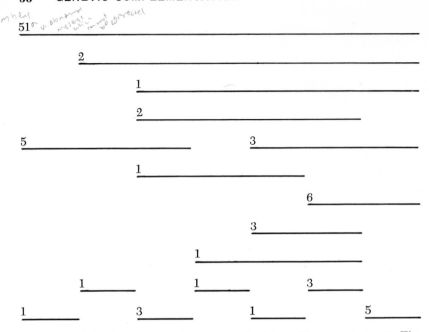

FIGURE 3-2 Complementation map of *ad-4* in *Neurospora crassa*. The number over each bar is the total number of auxotrophs from all sources which fall in that complementation group. From Woodward, Partridge, and Giles (1958).

to deletions of short chromosome segments. Such an explanation can be ruled out in at least some cases. Not only are many noncomplementing mutants capable of mutating back to something resembling the standard wild type (a very suggestive fact but not a conclusive one, since it is always difficult to rule out suppressor mutation as a cause of apparent reversion), but in several instances fine-structure mapping of the mutational sites definitely shows that deletions are not involved. This argument is dealt with in the next section.

Functional overlaps appearing as points on the genetic map. In several loci showing some interallelic complementation the linear order along the chromosome of the complementing and noncomplementing mutant sites has been determined. This is not the place to describe the fine-structure mapping techniques used for the ordering of closely linked sites; the interested reader is referred to recent reviews (Fincham and Day, 1965; Hayes, 1964). Perhaps the best examples for purposes of illustration are the *pan-2* (Figure 3-3), *ad-8* (Figure 3-4), and *tryp-3* (Figure 3-8) mutants of *Neurospora crassa*, and the *ad-6* mutants of *Schizosaccharomyces pombe* (Figure 5-1; Gutz, 1963). In each of these examples there is a numerous class of

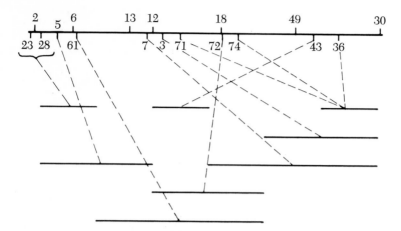

FIGURE 3-3   Complementation map of *pan-2* in *Neurospora crassa* compared with the genetic map (above). The numbers on the
genetic map are the isolation numbers of the mutants at
the sites indicated. Mutants above the line do not complement any other member of the series. Mutants below
the line are shown connected by broken lines to the
corresponding segment of the complementation map.
Redrawn from the data of Case and Giles (1960). Only
some of the genetic sites and complementation classes
are shown. The total length of the genetic map shown is
about 1 map unit (i.e., 1% recombination).

mutants, complementing neither with each other nor with any of the
complementing classes, which map at points scattered more or less
all through the locus. There are other mutants, represented on the
complementation map as partial rather than complete overlaps,
which also map as points.

By saying that these mutants map as points one means, first, that
in no case do they fail to show recombination with groups of other
mutants which recombine with each other, and, second, that the frequencies of recombination which they show with other mutants are
consistent with a reasonable additivity of map intervals, implying
that the sites marking these intervals are of negligible length (cf.
Figures 3-3 and 3-4).

One might attempt to explain the overlaps on the complementation maps by supposing that some point mutations "delete" the
function of the chromosome over an extended continuous segment
including, but much longer than, the mutational site itself. Some of
the data for the *Neurospora pan-2* locus are inconsistent with such
an idea. For example, mutants 36 and 7 are noncomplementary and
thus, if the functional deletion hypothesis were valid, the function

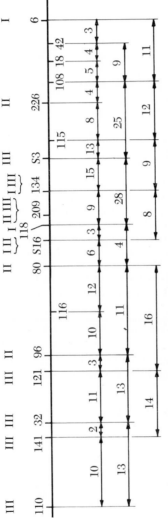

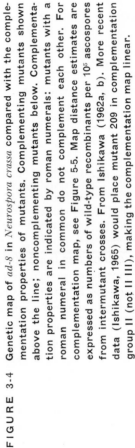

FIGURE 3-4   Genetic map of *ad-8* in *Neurospora crassa* compared with the complementation properties of mutants. Complementing mutants shown above the line; noncomplementing mutants below. Complementation properties are indicated by roman numerals: mutants with a roman numeral in common do not complement each other. For complementation map, see Figure 5-5. Map distance estimates are expressed as numbers of wild-type recombinants per 10^5 ascospores from intermutant crosses. From Ishikawa (1962a, b). More recent data (Ishikawa, 1965) would place mutant 209 in complementation group II (not II III), making the complementation map linear.

of the entire segment falling between these two sites would have to be deleted. In fact, however, mutant 43, which maps between 36 and 7, complements both (Figure 3-3). Woodward's (1962) analysis of the *pyr-3* mutants of *Neurospora* showed even more inconsistencies between the recombinational and complementation maps.

A somewhat analogous situation is found at the *dumpy* locus of *Drosophila melanogaster*. Mutants falling within this short chromosome segment give a variety of phenotypic effects. Several *dumpy* alleles cause, when homozygous, a shortening and *oblique* spreading of the wings (Figure 3-5), others cause a transverse rather than a longitudinal alignment of some of the thoracic bristles together with paired pits in the thorax ("*vortex*" effect), while yet others show both effects. Other alleles behave as recessive lethals, that is, they cannot be made homozygous, but can be shown to have recessive *oblique* or *vortex* effects in heterozygous compounds with nonlethal alleles showing these effects. In a sense these mutants show complementation, but, in general, only to the extent expected from a simple addition of the effects of the individual alleles (see Table 3-1).

Carlson (1959b) has mapped the sites of these various mutations of the *dumpy* series in a linear order; so far as can be determined they all map as points (Figure 3-5). It is obvious from the map that the *dumpy* region cannot be regarded as two or more discrete units of function. Not only do several of the mutations have two or three of the distinct effects on the phenotype, but the sites of mutations having a given effect in common do not necessarily fall within the same segment of the map. In particular, a number of mutant sites associated with the *vortex* effect span a site associated only with the *oblique* effect. It is not possible to say what the developmental rela-

TABLE 3-1 Phenotypes Expressed in *Drosophila* Carrying Various Combinations of *dumpy* Alleles †

Allele ‡	1^m	ol^s	olv^1	o^2	lv^1	ov^1	v^2	+
l^m	l	l	l	+	l	+	+	+
ol^s		l	l	o	l	o	+	+
olv^1			l	o	l	ov	v	+
o^2				o	+*	o	+	+
lv^1					l	v	v	+
ov^1						ov	v	+
v^2							v	+
+								+

† From Carlson, 1959b.
‡ *o* = *oblique; l* = *lethal; v* = *vortex;* * = blistered wings.

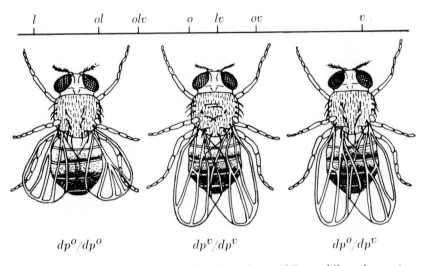

FIGURE 3-5   Genetic map of the *dumpy* locus of *Drosophila melanogaster* (after Carlson, 1959a), showing the positions of mutants giving the recessive *lethal* (*l*), *oblique* (*o*) and *vortex* (*v*) effects. The amount of recombination between the ends of the map as shown is about 0.1%. Below are shown (left to right) flies homozygous for *oblique* (*dp°*) and *vortex* (*dp^v*) alleles, and the *dp°/dp^v* heterozygote.

tionship between the *vortex, oblique,* and *lethal* effects is, but it is difficult to interpret the *dumpy* region other than as a single gene whose product is somehow involved in the development of the thorax of the fly. Another locus in *Drosophila* where different mutations can have different and sometimes apparently nonoverlapping effects, but which nevertheless does not seem to subdivide into functionally distinct genes, is *notch,* studied by Welshons and von Halle (1952).

To summarize, complementation maps of many loci, and the comparison, where it can be made, with the genetic map, are not easily reconciled with the view that such loci are segmented into regions of distinct and independent function. The entire locus, in each case, behaves in many ways as a functional unit.

Unitary biochemical function. Much argument about whether a given genetic segment is a unit of function or not can be dispensed with if the function can actually be analyzed in biochemical terms. Such an analysis is not available in all cases, but where it is it seems that there is indeed a single function. This function seems in general to be the control of the structure of a single enzymic protein. There are a large number of loci in microorganisms where complementation between some mutants is known to occur, and yet all the mutants seem to affect the activity of the same enzyme. In many of these cases the effects on activity are known to be due to qualitative changes in the structure of the protein.

Until an enzyme has been purified it is possible to suppose that the activity attributed to it is really due to the joint action of two or more proteins. Purification to the point where the activity can be shown to reside in one apparently homogeneous protein has been achieved in *Neurospora* for adenylosuccinase, controlled by *ad-4*, the nicotinamide adenine dinucleotide phosphate (NADP)-linked glutamate dehydrogenase (*am*), argininosuccinase (*arg-10*), and tryptophan synthetase (*tryp-3* or *td*), while in *Escherichia* coli the same can be said for alkaline phosphatase, controlled by the *p* locus, and β-galactosidase, controlled by the *z* segment of the *lac* region. It is clearly desirable to carry the analysis further, and to determine whether any of these enzymes are *heteromultimers*, that is, composed of polypeptide chains of more than one kind. The most obvious way in which two mutants, each defective in an enzyme activity, could complement to form active enzyme would be for one mutant to supply one polypeptide chain and the other to supply another of a different type. Such an explanation does actually apply in the famous case of *Escherichia coli* tryptophan synthetase, which consists of two dissimilar proteins complexed together (Yanofsky, 1960).

Evidence that complementation can occur between mutants, each defective in a monomeric or *homo*multimeric enzyme, is perhaps not conclusive in any example, but in a few cases it is fairly strong.

As Garen and Garen (1963) and Schlesinger, Torriani, and Levinthal (1963) have shown, complementation occurs between certain pairs of *p* mutants of *E. coli* with the formation of alkaline phosphatase superior in activity to the mutant varieties of the enzyme which the mutants form individually. The homogeneous native protein has a molecular weight of approximately 80,000 but at pH 4 it dissociates into subunits of approximately half that size (Schlesinger and Levinthal, 1963). Rothman and Byrne (1963), on the basis of the known amino acid composition of the protein and the hypothesis of one kind of polypeptide chain of weight 40,000, predicted the total number of different peptides (and the numbers which should contain arginine, histidine, and tyrosine, respectively) which should be yielded by digestion with trypsin. "Fingerprinting" analysis of tryptic digests showed numbers close to those predicted. Thus it seems almost certain that the native protein consists of two identical polypeptide chains, though there remains the possibility, very difficult to exclude without a complete sequence analysis, that the two chains are slightly different with the greater part of their amino acid sequence in common.

Somewhat similar evidence is available for the *Neurospora* glutamate dehydrogenase controlled by the *am* locus. Here the molecular weight of the native protein is about 260,000 (Barratt, 1961; Fincham and Coddington, 1963b). In solutions containing 6 M urea, or 0.1% sodium dodecyl sulfate (SDS), the protein dissociates into much smaller subunits; the molecular weight of the SDS subunit has been determined as about 50,000, but this may be an overestimate since no correction was made for the possible contribution of bound SDS. The subunits appeared homogeneous in the analytical ultracentrifuge. The amino acid analysis, combined with the numbers and kinds of peptides obtained after trypsin digestion, suggests that the protein is built out of identical polypeptide chains of about 30,000 molecular weight. This conclusion is subject to the same reservation as was made in the case of alkaline phosphatase, and there is the additional doubt here as to whether the 30,000-molecular-weight subunit is in fact the ultimate one. One cannot be sure that there are not two kinds of polypeptide, with a joint weight of 30,000, but this seems rather improbable. End-group analysis, which should give relevant information, has so far proved difficult for this protein.

The case of β-galactosidase in *Escherichia coli* may be more complicated. The enzyme certainly consists of identical subunits, but these subunits themselves appear to consist of more than one nonidentical polypeptide chain. Until recently β-galactosidase was thought to be composed of identical chains coded for by one cistron, the z gene. Complementation between different z mutants was known (Perrin, 1963), but the pattern of complementation was not obviously suggestive of a subdivision of the z segment into distinct cistrons (Perrin, 1963). The enzyme is obtainable in pure form with a molecular weight of about 540,000 (Craven, Steers, and Anfinsen, 1965). Zipser (1963a, b) found that it could be dissociated in 8 M urea into subunits which reassociated to form active enzyme on removal of the urea by dialysis. He carried out an ingenious experiment in which a small amount of purified highly radioactive (^{35}S-labeled) enzyme was mixed with a large excess of nonradioactive enzyme made unusually dense through incorporation of ^{13}C and ^{15}N. The mixture was dissociated with urea, and the urea was removed. In the reaggregated mixture it was shown by density gradient centrifugation that the radioactivity was now all present in a homogeneous class of molecules which had a density corresponding to three parts of "heavy" to one part of "light" material. This is just what would be expected if the protein consisted of four identical subunits which reassociated at random following urea dissociation; the large excess of heavy protein would ensure that virtually all the radioactive subunits would find themselves associated with three nonradioactive heavy ones. Since the hybrid material appeared to be uniform in molecular weight it seems likely that the four subunits are identical.

This conclusion is supported by considerable chemical data. Cohn (1957) estimated one N-terminal threonine residue per 125,000 molecular weight, and, more recently, Koorajian and Zabin (1965) have found one C-terminal lysine residue per 130,000 molecular weight. Investigations of the numbers of peptides formed by treatment with trypsin or with cyanogen bromide (which cleaves polypeptide chains adjacent to methionine residues) showed, given the overall amino acid composition, that there were enough *different* peptides to account for the 130,000 molecular weight subunit (Steer *et al.*, 1965). Any smaller subunits would have to be nonidentical. But Wallenfels, Sund, and Weber (1963) and Steers *et al.* (1965) showed that the 130,000 subunit could be further dissociated, by oxidation or reduction and carboxymethylation of the half-cystine residues followed by treatment with acid, alkali, or detergent, into smaller subunits of average molecular weight 40,000–50,000. It thus seems that each 130,000 subunit must consist of two or, more likely, three *different* chains, perhaps held together by disulfide bridges.

The genetic aspects of the situation have also been reappraised by Ullman *et al.* (1965). The arrangement of relevant sites of mutation in the z segment, and the portions of the segment which are missing in some deletion mutants, are shown in Table 3-2 together with some complementation data. The most significant fact is that the deletion mutant $B9$, missing a genetic segment extending from the left (operator) end of z to more than half way to the right end, complements strongly with a group of point mutants mapping at the right end. Mutant $B9$ was shown to produce a peptide, called the omega peptide, which would react with some component(s) of extracts of mutant $S908$ (mapping at the right end) to form active β-galactosidase. This same peptide, which was of molecular weight approximately 30,000–40,000, was also found in extracts of mutants carrying deletions of smaller extent as well as in the point mutant 1, so it seems likely to be a normal product of the right end of the z segment. The left-hand part of the segment, covered by the $B9$ deletion, seems likely to code for at least one other peptide component of the enzyme. The $B9$ region may actually code for two peptides, since mutants such as $M15$ and 05 with deletions confined to the more extreme left-hand end of z will complement point mutants, such as *359*, included in the right-hand end of the *B9* deletion (cf. Table 3-2). Even accepting this new interpretation there are still some anomalies in the complementation results to be explained (cf. p. 49), and the limits of the different cistrons within *z* do not yet seem to have been fixed with certainty. On the whole, this classical gene-enzyme system seems more likely to provide examples of intergenic than of interallelic complementation.

The available evidence taken as a whole makes it difficult to avoid the conclusion that some units of genetic material which are not strictly cistrons, since complementation occurs within them, do nevertheless specify the structure of single polypeptide chains.

Incompleteness of complementation. The tendency of this chapter so far is to suggest that there are indeed chromosomal segments, each concerned with specifying the structure of a single type of polypeptide chain, but that such segments are not necessarily

TABLE 3-2 Complementation between *z⁻* Mutants of *Escherichia coli,* and a Map of the *z* Region †

operator	84	2	4	1	359	178	908	181	177	*y* (*permease gene*)

M15
05
B9
02

Mutation on episome	Mutation on chromosome					
	1(a)	*4*(a)	*359*(b)	*178*(c)	*908*(c)	*181*(c)
M15(a)				2500	1855	
05(a)			155	871	985	1276
1(a)	0		0**	2500*		
4(a)	0	0	869	5070*		
177(c)	4450	1170	188	0		
B9(a+b)			0	1500	920	980
02(a+b+c)					0	0

† Data from Perrin (1963) and Ullmann *et al.* (1965). Numbers in the body of the table are specific activities of β-galactosidase measured in heterogenotes each carrying one *z* mutant on the chromosome and another on the F′ episome. Zero means less than 20. Letters in parentheses following mutant numbers indicate the hypothetical cistrons affected by each mutant. The extents of deletion mutants are indicated by brackets in the map at the head of the table. F′ cells with a wild type *z* segment on both chromosome and episome would give a specific activity of about 20,000 under the same conditions. * Indicates enzyme activity shown to be abnormally thermolabile. The result marked by ** does not fit the interpretation in terms of three cistrons adopted here.

cistrons in the original sense. They do, however, share with "true" cistrons the property of being definable by noncomplementary relationships of mutants; but the situation is not necessarily that *none* of the pairwise combinations of mutants complement, but rather that the whole set of mutants is connected by a series of overlapping noncomplementary relationships, with no clean division into mutually noncomplementing groups. Whether we call such a unit a cistron or not, we may as well call it a gene, and its mutant derivatives allelic, since it seems as good a functional unit as it is possible to define.

It is reasonable to suggest that though *some* degree of complementation may often occur between mutant derivatives, or alleles, of the same gene, such complementation is never complete in the sense of resulting in a gene product qualitatively similar to that of the wild-type gene. If this generalization is valid, then all the loci, or genes, which we have been considering in this chapter (with the probable exception of z in *E. coli*) could very well be cistrons if the cistron is defined by reference to the *cis-trans* position effect rather than by negative complementation tests. For if the *trans* genotype $m_1 +/+ m_2$ produces a partially functional but nonwild-type gene product, while the *cis* genotype $m_1 m_2/+ +$ produces at least a proportion of fully functional wild-type gene product, then we still have the position effect, even though the *trans* compound produces a more functional product than would either homozygous or haploid mutant by itself. The difficulty with this argument is that its verification may depend on knowing about the nature of the gene product. Incomplete complementation is often shown by subnormal growth. Tables 3-3 and 3-4 show examples from bacteriophage and *Neurospora*, respectively. But this is by no means always the case. Many interallelic combinations give growth hardly or not at all inferior to that of the wild-type organism, and in this respect the result is not distinguishable from intergenic complementation.

It is quite usual to find different degrees of complementation between different pairs of mutants within the same series, some pairs giving very little, and others apparently complete, complementation. Such a situation can sometimes be recognized by visual inspection of phenotypes. A good example is the *miniature-dusky* series in *Drosophila melanogaster,* studied by Dorn and Burdick (1962). Both *miniature (m)* and *dusky (dy)* alleles cause a shortening of the wing when homozygous. Most heteroallelic combinations of m mutants show some slight degree of complementation, as do several pairwise combinations within the dy group. Complementation between m and dy mutants is practically complete. One mutant, m^D, which causes some reduction in wing length even in combination with a

TABLE 3-3 Complementation between *rIIA* Mutants of Bacteriophage T4 *

	rF117	r553	r1451	r844	rC168	r490	r904	r104	rA69	r926	r476
rF117	0.006	0.02	0.27	1.3	0.90	**0.37**	**0.07**	**0.12**	**0.27**	3.1	2.7
r553		0.01	0.26	0.31	0.15	0.03	**0.08**	**0.11**	**0.11**	**0.19**	0.91
r1451			1.1	1.8	1.3	1.3	1.7	**8.2**	**3.1**	**4.4**	2.4
r844				1.7	1.1	1.3	2.1	1.6	**13.**	**4.8**	26.
rC168					0.74	0.44	0.44	0.61	**8.7**	**2.3**	26.
r490						0.008	0.02	0.03	0.02	0.01	1.3
r904							0.02	0.02	**0.33**	**0.60**	7.9
r104								0.02	0.02	0.01	0.87
rA69									0.03	**0.30**	8.5
r926										0.02	2.3
r476											2.7

* The table shows burst sizes from mixed infections of *E. coli* K12 (λ) as percent of burst size given by wild-type T4. In the diagonal are the values for each mutant alone; note that these complementing mutants are, in general, slightly "leaky." Combinations judged to show significant complementation are shown in bold type. Several experiments were required for all of the tests in the matrix; these varied somewhat in the exact burst sizes obtained, but agreed in consistently showing either complementation or not for each pair of mutants. The values shown are representative. Compare intercistronic complementation between *rII A* and *B* mutants (Table 2-1). The data can be represented by a complementation map in the form of a closed loop; omission of *r476* would permit representation by an open line. Data from S. E. Champe and S. Benzer, personal communication.

wild-type chromosome, is poorly complementary both with *m* and with *dy* alleles. All the mutants map genetically within a segment 0.06 map units long with the *m* mutants near one end, the *dy* mutants near the other, and with m^D in an intermediate position. The degree of complementation between two mutants seems to be related to their degree of separation on the map. One can interpret these results as meaning that *m* and *dy* are two different genes, with m^D some sort of structural chromosome change overlapping the two, or as one gene showing a wide range of different grades of complementation between its alleles. On either interpretation, incomplete complementation is a feature of the situation. Fahmy and Fahmy (1959) have reported incomplete complementation between certain pairs of *rudimentary* alleles in *Drosophila*, as well as virtually complete complementation between other pairs.

In other cases in *Drosophila*, interallelic complementation, if it is recognizable at all, gives a normal phenotype; complementation at

TABLE 3-4 Dry Weight Yields of Heterokaryons between *Neurospora tryp-3* Mutants *

	Mutant no.									
	72	**42**	**113**	**18**	**69**	**74**	**102**	**73**	**45**	**78**
72	0	0	0	24	27	27	50	tr	34	26
	42	0	0	0	0	0	0	0	0.2	tr
		113	0	0	0	0	0	0	21	tr
			18	0	0	0	0	0	0.1	1
				69	0	0	0	0	1	tr
					74	0	0	0	0.3	0.2
						102	0	0	0.4	tr
							73	0	0	0
								45	0	0
									78	0

* From Ahmad and Catcheside (1960); yields expressed as percentages of the yield of wild type.

Growth was in shaken liquid minimal medium for a standard length of time from a standard inoculum. The mutants were not the same as those used by Kaplan, Suyama, and Bonner (cf. Figure 3-8) except for 78, which is the same as 201 of Kaplan *et al.* Both 78 and 45 grow on indole as well as on tryptophan.

the *dumpy* (*dp*) locus, for example, results in the development of structures indistinguishable from those of the wild-type fly (cf. Figure 3-5). One must remember, however, that phenotype, at the level of growth on minimal medium, or morphology, can be a very insensitive measure of what is happening to the enzyme which is the primary protein product of the gene. For example, Donachie (1964) has shown that in *Neurospora* the level of argininosuccinase can be reduced to less than 5% of the wild-type value without causing a demonstrable requirement for arginine. Where, in fact, interallelic complementation has been studied at the enzyme level, the generalization that it is always incomplete seems to hold good, with some doubtful exceptions. This point is well made by one study in *Drosophila. Maroon-like* (*ma-l*) mutants have yellow-orange rather than dark red eyes, and they lack active xanthine dehydrogenase. Glassman and Pinkerton (1960) showed that flies heteroallelic for a certain pair of *ma-l* mutants had eyes of wild-type color, but their level of xanthine dehydrogenase activity was only about 5% of the normal value.

Information on the amount of enzyme activity formed as a result of interallelic complementation, in comparison with the amount formed by the wild-type allele, is available in several cases. In *Neu-*

rospora, both Woodward *et al.* (1958), working with adenylosuccinase controlled by *ad-4,* and Fincham (1959), working with glutamate dehydrogenase (*am*), found that even the best interallelic pairs
formed no more than about 25% of the level of enzyme activity normally found in the wild type, and many formed much smaller
amounts. As we shall see in the next chapter, there is no *general*
theoretical reason for expecting an upper limit of 25% and, indeed,
Garen and Garen 1963 (see Table 3-5) found one pair of mutant *p*
alleles in *E. coli* which would complement to the extent of 67% of
wild-type alkaline phosphatase activity, though most of their complementing combinations were considerably less effective than this.

Perhaps more convincing than the general tendency of interallelic
combinations to form only relatively low *amounts* of enzyme activity
is the observation, made in a number of different systems, that enzyme formed as a result of interallelic complementation is *qualitatively* different from the wild-type enzyme. Fincham (1959), Partridge (1961), Suyama and Bonner (1964), Garen and Garen (1963),
and Gross and Webster (1963) have all demonstrated, in their own
respective experimental systems, that a reduced thermostability as
compared with the corresponding wild-type enzyme is a common
feature of enzyme formed by interallelic complementation. Table
3-5 summarizes Garen and Garen's data. The degree of instability
observed depends on the particular pair of mutants, and both Par-

TABLE 3-5   Activity and Heat Sensitivity of Alkaline Phosphatase Produced by Complementation between
Phosphatase-Negative Mutants of *Escherichia
coli* *

F' strain		Initial enzyme activity as % of haploid wild type	Surviving enzyme activity (% after 20 min at 91°C)
Episome	Chromosome		
Wild type	Wild type	240	100
U9	E32a	161	100
U9	U32	60	75
U9	U57	27	38
U9	S33	50	3
S6	U57	110	5
S6	S33	101	3
E15	G41	3	1

* From Garen and Garen, 1963.

tridge and the Garens found that some complementing pairs gave enzyme of apparently normal stability. Fincham, Suyama and Bonner, and Gross and Webster also detected abnormalities in Michaelis and other kinetic constants in enzymes formed by complementation. The significance of these qualitative abnormalities will be discussed more fully in the next chapter. Here it will suffice to point out that a failure to detect any abnormality of enzyme properties in one or a few tests does not, of course, prove that there is no abnormality present, and the fact that differences in properties can be so easily detected in so many of the enzymes formed by interallelic complementation makes it seem rather likely that some degree of abnormality is always present in such enzyme molecules. If this is, indeed, a valid general rule, it provides, in principle, a definition of allelism and a modified definition of the cistron or gene.

The need for some caution in interpreting findings of enzyme abnormality is, however, indicated by some of the data on the *E. coli* β-galactosidase system. Perrin (1963) showed that complementation between various pairs of z^- mutants gave β-galactosidase activity which was low compared with wild type, or abnormally thermolabile, or both (cf. Table 3-2). Yet the more recent studies of Ullmann *et al.* (1965) suggest that many or all of these cases involve complementation between different polypeptide chains controlled by different cistrons within the z region. This is puzzling at first sight since one would expect complementation between mutants defective in different polypeptide chains to give a qualitatively normal protein product. The answer to this anomaly may lie in the peculiar structure of the enzyme molecule. β-Galactosidase, as we have seen, probably consists of four identical subunits each consisting of two or three nonidentical chains. Complementation between different kinds of nonmutant chains could result in the formation of completely normal subunits, but the latter could still aggregate with subunits containing mutant chains. Suppose, for the sake of simplicity, there are two chains per subunit, one called *alpha* (α) and the other *omega* (Ω). A mutant with defective *alpha* (a^1) would complement another with defective *omega* (Ω^2) since the latter would produce normal *alpha* (a^+) and the former normal *omega* (Ω^+). The heterogenote carrying both mutant *lac* segments would produce four kinds of subunit, $a^1\Omega^+$, $a^+\Omega^2$, $a^1\Omega^2$, and $a^+\Omega^+$, the last being completely normal. But formation of tetramers at random would give a large number of different kinds of hybrid (actually 35 in all), of which only the one with four $a^+\Omega^+$ subunits would be completely normal in structure. Some of the others might be practically normal in activity and stability but many of the hybrids might well be abnormal by either or both of these criteria because of their content of mutant chains. This explanation fits well with Perrin's (1963) observation that the enzyme formed by complementation was in some cases obviously heterogeneous with respect to thermostability. While this explanation seems satisfactory in one sense, it suggests the need for considerable caution in distinguishing inter- from intracistronic complementation, even where one has information about the relevant enzyme activities and stabilities. A formal *cis-trans* comparison should always make the distinction but, for reasons explained previously, this is often impossibly laborious to apply to more than a very few mutant combinations.

In practice, and where one has relatively complete complementation data for a fairly large number of mutants, one can usually arrive at a highly probable interpretation even without any detailed biochemical information. The general rule followed is that mutants belonging in different genes always complement, whereas mutants in the same gene, while they may sometimes complement, are always noncomplementary with other point mutants belonging in the same gene. In other words, the continuous overlaps on the complementation map define the gene.

Unfortunately, exclusive reliance on overlaps in the complementation map of a genetic region may, in special cases, lead to incorrect judgments. This is due to the fact that, as is now realized, there may be units of coordinated function in a chromosome of a higher order than single genes. The remainder of this chapter will deal with cases of this sort.

3-2 DISTINGUISHING BETWEEN GENES AND OPERONS

The operon hypothesis of Jacob and Monod (1961a, b) is now well known, and a detailed account of its derivation seems unnecessary. I will merely summarize the main points of the hypothesis as it applies to the system on which it was originally based, the *lac* mutants of *Escherichia coli*.

The *lac* mutants of *E. coli*. To utilize lactose, *E. coli* cells must be able to form β-galactosidase. To utilize it with any degree of efficiency, they must also be able to form a specific mechanism for taking up the sugar from the medium. This uptake component, or permease, is thought to be a protein located in the cell membrane. Most mutants unable to grow with lactose as sole carbon source are either defective in β-galactosidase (z^- mutants) or in the permease (y^- mutants). These two classes of mutants map in separate but adjacent genetic segments, the z and the y. The galactosidase and permease, together with a third protein of obscure metabolic function, galactoside transacetylase, are normally only formed in appreciable amounts in response to induction by the presence in the growth medium of lactose or any one of several lactose analogues. Under many conditions of induction (Jacob and Monod, 1961b), though not all (Zabin, 1963), the galactosidase and transacetylase, and probably the permease as well, are formed in constant ratio, as if some rate-determining step was common to the synthesis of all three. This step is thought to be the formation, or possibly the translation, of a messenger RNA molecule common to the whole *lac* region, including z and y and presumably another gene controlling the transacetylase. The *lac* region is regarded as an example of an *operon*, a unit of genetic transcription which may include several cistrons.

A third class of lactose-negative mutants is unable to produce β-galactosidase or permease or transacetylase. These mutants fail to complement in heterogenotes either with z^- or with y^- mutants. Genetically these mutants map close to one end of the z gene, on the side distant from y, and were called *o*-zero (o^o), being attributed to another genetic element called o (operator), which was considered to be involved in initiating the transcription of the entire operon. Mapping quite close to the o^o mutant sites was another class of mutants called *o*-constitutives (o^c) which had the property of producing all of the three proteins controlled by the *lac* region regardless of whether inducer was present or not; this uncontrolled activity was shown only by a *lac* region in coupling with the o^c mutation on the same chromosome, and did not extend to *lac* carried on a separate genetic fragment in a heterogenote. The o segment was considered to be involved in the initiation of messenger formation, with o^o mutations preventing such initiation under all conditions and o^c mutations rendering it independent of the normal regulatory mechanism.

Subsequent observations have thrown some doubt, not so much on whether there is a genetic segment controlling the initiation of transcription, but on whether the o^o mutations necessarily fall within it (Stent, 1964). One finding which has complicated the picture is that certain mutations ("polarity mutants") within z which abolish the galactosidase activity also cause a reduction, which may be drastic in some mutants, of the *quantity* of permease and transacetylase which is formed. Similarly, some permease-negative (y^-)

mutants, while they all have a normal potential for producing galactosidase, produce little or no transacetylase. This points to a polarized transcription or translation of the *lac* region starting from the *o* end and proceeding to the hypothetical gene beyond *y* controlling transacetylase. It seems that certain mutants falling within a gene, and having their primary effects on the protein controlled by that gene, can cause a reduction in the efficiency of the transcription or translation of the message from that point on. In the light of this hypothesis there is no compelling reason for regarding the o^o mutants as other than z^- mutants with extreme effects on the polarized reading of the *lac* region. Beckwith (1964) has, indeed, obtained convincing evidence in favor of such an interpretation.

Regardless of how one interprets the o^o mutants, they, with the polarity mutants, illustrate that mutations which map as points within one gene can have profound effects on the activity of neighboring genes.

There are several other well-authenticated examples in bacteria of mutations having polar effects within operons. Englesberg and his colleagues have studied mutants of *E. coli* unable to utilize arabinose. Such mutants, of which there are many, can be grouped into four genes or cistrons, three of which, *A*, *B*, and *D*, appear to be concerned with the determination of the structure of the first three enzymes of arabinose catabolism, respectively L-arabinose isomerase, L-ribulokinase, and L-ribulose 5-phosphate 4-epimerase (Englesberg, 1961; Englesberg *et al.*, 1962). The fourth gene, *C*, can mutate to cause an inability to form all three enzymes and also a specific arabinose permease, but such mutations do not resemble the o^o type of the *lac* series since their effects can be overcome by the presence in a zygote of a normal *C* gene on a separate piece of genetic material (Helling and Weinberg, 1963). It seems that *C* must be somehow concerned with producing something essential for the induction of the three enzymes and the permease, which are formed only in response to an inducer, normally arabinose. All four genes are closely linked and adjacent in the order *D–A–B–C* (Gross and Englesberg, 1959; Englesberg *et al.*, 1962) and the whole region seems to be an operon in that the levels of the three enzymes seem to be coordinately controlled (Lee and Englesberg, 1963). The situation is summarized in Fig. 3-6.

The most interesting feature of the arabinose system is the effect of mutations within one gene on the level of activity of another within the operon. Lee and Englesberg (1962) showed that mutations within gene *A*, with the primary effect of altering the structure

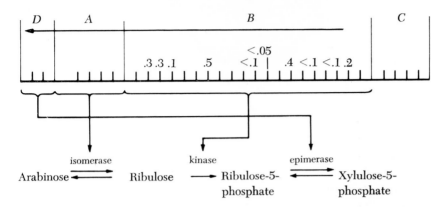

FIGURE 3-6 Genetic map of mutants of *Escherichia coli* unable to utilize arabinose, showing the positions of the segments controlling three enzymes of arabinose catabolism. Several mutations in gene B, controlling primarily the structure of the kinase, cause a quantitative reduction in the levels of the isomerase and epimerase. The proportion of the normal levels to which these two enzymes are reduced is indicated over the site of each mutation having such an effect. The other mutations in B either have no effect on isomerase and epimerase levels or somewhat increase them. Mutant sites are shown evenly spaced for ease of representation. After Lee and Englesberg (1963); for further details see text.

and eliminating the activity of the isomerase, also caused an increase in the production of the kinase. Conversely, some mutants in the *B* gene, with structural alterations in the kinase, produced unusually large amounts of isomerase. These effects can perhaps be regarded as due to the operation of some as yet obscure compensatory mechanism. However, some mutants in the *B* gene, in fact about half of them, formed *reduced* amounts of isomerase, the reduction being almost to zero in some cases (Cribbs and Englesberg, 1964). Where the level of epimerase has been tested, it has been found to vary in parallel with that of the isomerase in response to mutation in *B* (Englesberg *et al.*, 1962). Furthermore, the formation of isomerase in *B* mutants is proportional to that of mutationally altered kinase as measured immunochemically. It seems that the activities of the whole group of genes in the operon are geared together, and that many mutants in *B* bring about a structural alteration *and* a change in rate of formation in the kinase, and simultaneously a proportionate

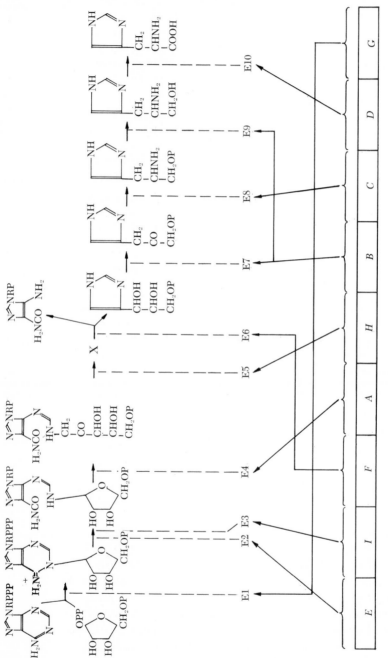

FIGURE 3-7 The nine genes of the *Salmonella typhimurium* "histidine" operon, represented arbitrarily as segments of equal length, controlling the ten enzymic activities (E1–E10) involved in histidine synthesis. E7 and E9 are probably activities of a single protein. After Ames and Hartman (1963). The information that E2 and E3 are separate enzymes (a pyrophosphorylase and a hydrolase) is from Ahmed *et al.*, quoting Ames (personal communication).

change in rate of formation *without* any structural change in the isomerase and epimerase, controlled by genes *A* and *D* to the left in the map. Some of the *B* mutants show such a large quantitative depression that they might easily give negative complementation tests with *A* and *D* (isomerase and epimerase) mutants, though data on this specific point are not available.

Another impressive case of polarity effects within an operon is provided by the histidine auxotrophs of *Salmonella* (Hartman, Loper, and Serman, 1960; Ames and Hartman, 1963). Figure 3-7 shows the close linkage of the nine genes, distinguished by biochemical and abortive transduction complementation tests, which almost certainly determine the structures of the eight or nine enzymes specifically concerned with histidine synthesis. Mutations falling within one of these genes commonly affect the enzyme controlled specifically by that gene, and no other. A number of mutants are known, however, which though mapping at single sites within genes, cause a quantitative depression in the levels of the enzymes controlled by all the genes to the left (as the map is drawn) of the mutational site, wherever it may be. Polarity mutants of this type have been identified in genes *A*, *B*, *C*, *D*, and *G* (cf. Figure 3-7). As in the case of the *ara* system of *E. coli* the depression in activity of the affected genes seems to be a coordinate one, with the activities of all the genes to the left of the mutational site reduced by the same proportion.

Operator and polarity-type mutants make any simple definition of a cistron virtually impossible. Among the *E. coli lac* mutants, for example, an o^o and a z^- (or y^-) mutant show a *cis-trans* position effect. The *cis* arrangement o^o z^-/o^+ z^+ gives a normal amount of β-galactosidase after induction, while the *trans* compound o^o z^+/o^+ z^- gives none. On the strict definition of the cistron, *o* and *z*, or *o* and *y*, are parts of the same cistron, although *z* and *y* are in different cistrons! Since we know in this case that *z* and *y* have different biochemical functions, it is clear that a strict adherence to the original cistron definition is likely to lead one astray in situations of the operon type. Perhaps the reluctance of some *Drosophila* geneticists to apply the cistron concept to their organism may, after all, have shown a sound instinct. Some of the pseudoallelic series in *Drosophila* may well turn out to correspond to operons rather than to cistrons, as has been suggested by Lewis (1963) for the *bithorax* series of mutants. But in the absence of information at the biochemical level the interpretation of many of these cases must remain in doubt.

One is driven to the conclusion that there is no simple rule of thumb for identifying the functional genetic unit. Each case has to be judged separately on the basis of combined enzymological and genetic data. In the remainder of this chapter, I will deal with some series of auxotrophic mutants in fungi whose interpretation should be re-examined in the light of the operon hypothesis.

Let us first consider the *tryp-3* mutants of *Neurospora,* already described on p. 47. Here there is a numerous class of noncomplementing mutants, but those which do complement include two enzymologically distinct classes. Several mutants (indole accumulators) produce protein immunologically related to tryptophan synthetase which is able to catalyze the reaction indoleglycerol phosphate → indole, but not the synthesis of tryptophan. There are also a few other mutants (indole utilizers) which produce an immunologically related protein which catalyzes the reaction indole + serine → trytophan. These two classes of mutants complement each other (cf. Figure 3-8). The situation is somewhat more complicated than this, inasmuch as some pairs of indole accumulators complement each other, but nevertheless it is reasonable to ask whether this case may not be one where there are two adjacent genes controlling two catalytically complementary enzymic proteins. Such an interpretation would bring *Neurospora* into line with *E. coli* (cf. pp. 30–31). There are two reasons why a two-gene hypothesis is not plausible in this case. First, the mutants producing *neither* enzyme activity map at points all through the *tryp-3* segment (Figure 3-8). Even though the localization of the indole-accumulator and indole-utilizer sites in two different regions might suggest a functional differention within the segment, the broad scatter of the noncomplementing sites makes it impossible to regard them either as operator-negative or as polarity mutations. One would have to invoke a two-way spreading effect, rather than a polarity effect, to explain how all these mutants could be deficient in the activity of both genes simultaneously. The second reason is that, though *Neurospora* tryptophan synthetase has been extensively purified (Carsiotis *et al.,* 1963; Bonner, 1963), no indication has been obtained that the enzyme consists of more than one protein component or more than one kind of polypeptide chain. At present it seems much more likely that *tryp-3* is a single gene controlling a single protein with one kind of polypeptide chain, having three assayable enzyme activities which can be affected differentially by mutation.

A second example in *Neurospora* leads to a different conclusion. Histidine-requiring mutants of the *hist-3* series have been investi-

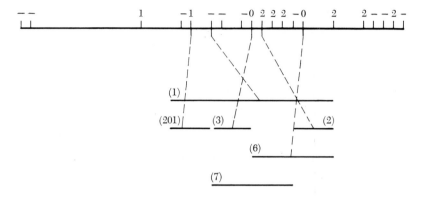

FIGURE 3-8   Genetic map of *tryp-3* of *Neurospora crassa* (after Kaplan, Suyama, and Bonner, 1964) in comparison with the complementation map (after Rachmeler and Yanofsky, 1961, and Lacy and Bonner, 1962). The genetic map is not drawn strictly to scale in that very close spacings have been increased for easier representation. The amount of recombination between the ends of the map as shown is about 0.4%. The symbols above the genetic sites mean as follows: —, mutant producing no protein (cross-reacting material = CRM) resembling tryptophan synthetase immunochemically; 0, mutant producing CRM with no enzyme activity; 1, mutant producing CRM catalyzing indole + serine→tryptophan only; 2, mutant producing CRM catalyzing indoleglycerol phosphate→triose phosphate + indole only. Mutants (isolation numbers in parenthesis) shown in the complementation map connected by dashed lines to positions on the genetic map, where known. Complementation produces a protein catalyzing the overall reaction indoleglycerol phosphate + serine→ tryptophan + triose phosphate.

gated both by Catcheside (1960) and by Webber (1960) and Webber and Case (1960). Both Catcheside and Webber found that some *hist-3* mutants accumulated histidinol, lacking histidinol dehydrogenase, which is the enzyme catalyzing the terminal step in histidine synthesis, while others were unable to carry out a much earlier step prior to the formation of the imidazole ring. Some members of this latter category were able to form histidinol dehydrogenase activity and complemented with any one of the histidinol accumulating mutants. Although all the *hist-3* mutants are closely linked it would have been natural to conclude that they represented two different genes, controlling two quite distinct enzymes, had it not been for the fact that many of the mutants blocked at the early step apparently lacked histidinol dehydrogenase too, and failed to complement with the histidinol accumulators. Catcheside's interpretation, which was plausible at the time, was that *hist-3* was one gene controlling one enzyme with two catalytic functions, which could be eliminated differentially by mutation. This is very similar to the explanation given above for the *tryp-3* mutants.

Recently, however, Ahmed, Case, and Giles (1964; see also Giles, 1965) have obtained further information which suggests that *hist-3* is really an operon comprising at least three genes. These workers now recognize three mutually complementing groups of mutants. Those in groups *hist-3A* and *hist-3B* are defective with respect to two different enzymes involved in the conversion of phosphoribosyl-adenosine triphosphate to phosphoribosyl-formimino-amino-imidazole-carboxamide-ribosyl phosphate; these two enzymes correspond respectively to E3 and E2 of Figure 3-7. Mutants in group *hist-3D* lack histidinol dehydrogenase. The three classes each fall within a distinct section of the gene map, in the order A–B–D. The class which appears to lack all three activities, and which fails to complement with either A, B, or D mutants, maps partly within A and partly to the left of A.[1] Thus it seems very likely that A, B, and D are three distinct genes coordinated in an operon, and that the completely noncomplementing mutants are polarity mutants or operator mutants or both. This conclusion is borne out by enzymological studies by Ahmed, which indicate that complementation between the postulated genes within *hist-3* is always complete, in the sense of yielding a normal amount of apparently normal enzyme, while complementation within *hist-3D* results in the formation of histidinol dehydrogenase with abnormal properties. An otherwise fairly tidy situation is complicated by the apparent existence of another segment C, falling between B and D, in which mutants appear to lack A, B, and D functions. Ahmed *et al.* suggest that this segment may control the structure of a polypeptide chain which is a component of both the "A" and the "B" enzymes, but these two enzymes have not been very well characterized and perhaps their existence as distinct proteins cannot yet be taken for granted. The present view of the situation at *hist-3* is summarized in Figure 3-9. This seems one of the best cases to date of an operon in an organism other than a bacterium.

A very similar choice of interpretations is offered by the situation at the *pyr-3* locus of *Neurospora* (Davis and Woodward, 1962) where, as at *hist-3*, there appear to be two enzymic functions which

---

[1] Though there is still some doubt on the mapping data (Catcheside, 1965).

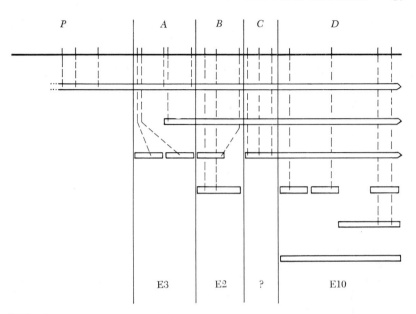

FIGURE 3-9   A possible operon in *Neurospora crassa*. The genetic map
of the *hist-3* region with mutant sites spaced approximately to scale is shown above; the entire segment shown
is about 0.07 map units long. Complementation relationships of the mutants are shown by the open bars of the
complementation map below. The positioning of some of
these bars is determined by other complementing mutants
which have not been mapped genetically and which are
not represented here. The bars ending in arrows represent
supposed polar effects of mutants in one structural gene
on the activities of genes to the right. Mutants confined
in their effects to *A, B,* and *D* lack enzymes E3, E2, and
E10 respectively (cf. Figure 3-7). Mutants in *P* lack all
three enzymes; *P* could be part of *A* or could be an
operator or "promoter" segment concerned with initiation
of transcription of the operon. Mutants in *C* apparently
lack all three enzymes. After Ahmed, Case, and Giles
(1964).

can be eliminated either separately or together by genetic mutation.
The mapping data do not altogether agree with the operon hypothesis in this case, but they are not really adequate to establish the order
of the mutational site with any degree of certainty (Suyama, Munkres, and Woodward, 1959).

   To summarize, one remains convinced that the genome *is* segmented into genes, each one of which is concerned with a single

function—in general, the synthesis of a particular polypeptide chain. But it no longer seems possible to formulate a simple definition of a gene which can be always relied upon in the absence of a detailed biochemical analysis. The original clear-cut definition of the cistron by Benzer did not take into account the widespread occurrence of interallelic complementation, and subsequent attempts to define a modified cistron on the basis of overlapping classes of noncomplementing mutants (e.g., Fincham and Day, 1965) are not adequate to deal with operon-like situations. However, as Giles (1965) has argued, intergene overlaps on the complementation map due to polarity or operator mutants may in principle be recognized by the polarized arrangement of the mutants concerned on the fine-structure genetic map, where the latter is available (cf. Figure 3-9). An enzymological study may still be needed to lend full conviction to the analysis.

It may be noted that genes do *not* appear to be functionally integrated into operons in the best-studied virus, bacteriophage T4, although there is some grouping of functionally related genes which is of uncertain significance (cf. p. 28). For this reason complementation tests are subject to fewer ambiguities in bacteriophage than in bacterial genetics.

In conclusion, it may be appropriate to give an example of a situation which at present seems quite ambiguous. Ramirez, Friis, and Leupold (1963) studied the complementation relationships of forty-six *ad-1* mutants of *Schizosaccharomyces pombe.* These mutants have a metabolic block or blocks relatively early in the pathway of adenine synthesis, but their biochemistry has not been worked out in detail. Their complementation relationships and their positions on a fine-structure genetic map are shown in Figure 3-10. One can see at once that were it not for the twelve mutants (at nine different sites) which fail to complement with all the others, the *ad-1* region would obviously be divided between two different genes. Twelve mutants (at ten sites) map in the right-hand section, and twenty-two others (at sixteen sites) in a relatively compact cluster to the left; these two nonoverlapping groups of mutant sites show intergroup complementation in all possible combinations of mutants, but no complementation, or only sporadic complementation, within themselves.[2] Could, then, the twelve completely noncomplementing mutants be operator or polarity mutants? The fact that they map at sites within *both* groups of complementing mutants seems incompatible

[2] For a similar but possibly more straightforward case in yeast, see Costello and Bevan (1964) and Dorfman (1964) on the *ad-5/7* locus.

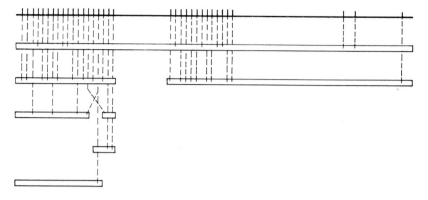

FIGURE 3-10   The genetic map, totalling about 0.1 map units, of the *ad-1* segment of *Schizosaccharomyces pombe* (above) compared with the complementation map (open bars, below). Mutant sites fall into the three groups as shown, but their spacing within these groups has been made arbitrarily regular for simplicity of representation. After Ramirez, Friis, and Leupold (1963); detailed data supplied by Leupold (personal communication).

with either of these suggestions. We are left with two possibilities. Either *ad-1* of *Schizosaccharomyces* is one gene determining the structure of one protein with two functions which are mutationally independent of each other to a surprising degree, or there are two genes, and mutations within one gene can affect the functioning of neighboring genes to *either* side. The latter possibility implies a nonpolarized spreading effect of point mutations, of a kind for which there is no apparent theoretical basis. The first alternative seems more appealing, but one should beware of assuming that our present theoretical models are adequate to account for every kind of interaction between neighboring genes.

4

THE MECHANISM OF INTERALLELIC
COMPLEMENTATION

The most interesting kind of interallelic complementation is that in which two alleles can together form an enzyme which neither could produce by itself. At the outset, however, we should consider whether complementation may not sometimes result from an independent action of different mutant alleles.

4-1 COMPLEMENTATION RESULTING FROM INDEPENDENT ACTION OF ALLELES

Such cases might be expected wherever a single enzyme, determined by a single gene, has two or more enzymic functions which can be affected independently by mutation. For example, among the *tryp-3* mutants of *Neurospora*, discussed in the preceding chapter, those which retain the ability to convert indoleglycerol phosphate to indole might be expected to complement those which have lost this function but which retain the ability to condense indole with serine (cf. Figure 3-8). Such complementation might be significant even without any interaction between the protein products of the mutant alleles. It is clear, however, that in this example the complementary pairs of alleles act in a more than merely additive fashion, since the tryptophan synthetase formed by complementation

catalyzes the overall reaction (indoleglycerol phosphate + serine →
tryptophan + phosphoglyceraldehyde) much more efficiently than
would a simple mixture of the two kinds of defective enzyme formed
by the mutants individually (Rachmeler and Yanofsky, 1961). In fact,
no certain examples of merely additive complementary action of
mutant allelic enzymes can be given at the present time.

Also hypothetical is the case in which two alleles contribute enzyme varieties having the *same* activity but functioning optimally
under different conditions. This possibility can be illustrated by the
mutant variety of glutamate dehydrogenase in *Neurospora* associated with the allele am^{3a} (Fincham and Bond, 1960). This variety
has a far higher Michaelis constant for ammonium ion than the wild-
type enzyme but a higher maximum activity at saturating ammonium concentrations. One can imagine conditions in which this
mutant enzyme would be more efficient than the wild-type enzyme
and others in which the converse would be true, so a heterokaryon
producing both might be at an advantage in certain kinds of fluctuat-
ing environment. It would be surprising, however, if such an effect
were clearly detectable in any simple growth test.

In *Drosophila* there are a number of cases in which alleles show
more or less additive complementation at the morphological level.
Two examples, which were mentioned in the last chapter, are the
scute and *dumpy* series of alleles, where allelic mutants sometimes
have nonoverlapping or only partially overlapping effects on the
phenotype; here complementation means merely that each allele is
contributing to the heterozygous fly those morphological structures
which it can determine by itself. Assuming that such loci as *scute*
and *dumpy* do control single enzymes (an assumption which is dis-
putable), one could explain the complementary effects of alleles in
either of the two ways mentioned in the preceding paragraphs. The
development of different morphological structures might depend on
different catalytic functions which can be affected differentially by
mutation though associated with a single enzyme. Alternatively the
conditions for activity of the enzyme concerned might be different
in different tissues, so that a change in the enzyme which made it
essentially inactive in one part of the fly might not have a critical
effect on its activity in another part. It is clear in principle that, in a
morphologically complex organism, alleles which represented, at the
enzyme level, changes in the same function could have end results
which appeared, at the morphological level, to indicate different
functions. No examples of this kind of situation have, however, been
demonstrated experimentally.

There are two examples in *Neurospora* of apparently complementary action depending on the striking of the right balance between an overactive and an inactive allele. The first was contributed by Emerson (1948), who investigated a mutant (*sfo*) with the curious property of requiring sulfanilamide for growth at 35° C. Various lines of evidence pointed to the conclusion that the sulfanilamide promoted growth by acting as an antagonist of *p*-aminobenzoic acid, which was, for some reason, toxic to *sfo* strains at the concentrations at which it is normally present in the mycelium. An *sfo* mycelium could be enabled to grow on minimal medium at 35°C through the introduction into a proportion of its nuclei of a second mutation (*paba*) blocking p-aminobenzoic acid synthesis. The balance of the two kinds of nuclei needed for optimum growth is rather a delicate one; with too few *paba* nuclei the mycelium poisons itself with its own *p*-aminobenzoic acid, whereas with too many it produces too little of the vitamin to be able to grow well. However, when mixed in the right proportion, the two alleles *paba* and *paba*+ can together promote growth in a situation where neither could do so alone.

Another case of a rather similar kind has been described by Reissig (1960). The *arg-2* mutants of *Neurospora* are, for some reason which is still obscure, unable to make adequate amounts of carbamoyl phosphate (CAP) for arginine synthesis. Some *pyr-3* mutations, which cause a loss of activity of aspartic transcarbamylase and a consequent inability to use CAP for pyrimidine synthesis, relieve the arginine requirement of *arg-2* mutants, apparently because CAP, the utilization of which is blocked in the pyrimidine pathway, becomes available for the arginine pathway (Davis and Woodward, 1962). A homokaryotic *arg-2 pyr-3*+ strain will only grow if supplied with arginine or citrulline; a homokaryotic *arg-2 pyr-3* strain requires a pyrimidine even though its arginine requirement is suppressed. A heterokaryon containing both kinds of nuclei will, if the nuclear ratio is within certain limits, make enough aspartic transcarbamylase to satisfy its pyrimidine requirement but still accumulate enough CAP to supply the arginine pathway. Here again, the mere dilution of a wild-type activity by the total inactivity of a defective mutant allele can, in a rather special genetic background, give a better-balanced metabolism than could either allele alone.

4-2 COMPLEMENTATION RESULTING IN THE FORMATION OF A NEW ENZYME ACTIVITY

Early observations. We shall be mainly concerned in this chapter with interallelic complementation resulting in the formation of some new enzyme activity which could not have been formed by either allele by itself. The first examples were obtained in *Neurospora* by Fincham and Pateman (1957) for glutamate dehydrogenase, controlled by the *am* locus, and by Giles, Partridge, and Nelson (1957) for adenylosuccinase, controlled by the *ad-4* locus. At the time it was not at all apparent how the formation of a new enzyme activity could be explained by interaction between preformed proteins or polypeptide chains, and it was natural to speculate that it might be due to some type of recombinational event occurring either during polypeptide synthesis or during the synthesis of the corresponding template RNA. Since complementation in *Neurospora* heterokaryons occurs between alleles in different nuclei, it could not be supposed that the recombination occurred between the genes themselves. It was suggested, however (Woodward *et al.*, 1958), that some kind of crossing-over might take place between allelic products either at the RNA or the polypeptide stage. This hypothesis was encouraged by the finding, in the adenylosuccinase case, that the yield of enzyme formed by interallelic complementation increased with the degree of separation of the mutant sites within the gene. Significance was also attached to the generalization, which held true in at least the first cases examined (but see Table 3-2), that interallelic complementation did not yield more than 25% of the normal wild-type level of enzyme activity, even with the most efficiently complementing pairs of alleles. This was compatible with the idea of a free reassortment of relatively widely separated segments of polypeptide or RNA chains, with a 25% yield of a wild-type recombinant strand as the limiting case.

In spite of its initial attractiveness, the crossover hypothesis is now generally discounted. The type of equal exchange process required has never been demonstrated except between molecules of genetic nucleic acid endowed with the capacity for self-replication. Furthermore, it soon became evident (Fincham, 1959; Partridge, 1961; Garen and Garen, 1963; Gross and Webster, 1963; Perrin, 1963) that enzyme formed by interallelic complementation was very often and perhaps always abnormal in its properties. To be sure, this abnormality could be explained as due to unequal crossing-over, but in most cases it seems that the enzyme formed is more or less homogeneous, with essentially no molecules with wild-type properties, whereas imprecision in crossing-over would be expected to yield a whole family of enzyme types with wild type making a substantial contribution to the active material. Finally, the crossing-over hypothesis is no longer necessary, since a much simpler and well-substantiated explanation for interallelic complementation now exists.

The hybrid protein hypothesis. The general explanation for

TABLE 4-1 Subunit Structure of Some Enzymes [*]

Enzyme	Aggregate (M.W.)	Subunit (M.W.)	No. of Subunits	Evidence for identical subunits	Reference
Liver glutamate dehydrogenase	10^6	ca. 4×10^4	18–24	Analysis of N-terminal groups	Jirgensons (1961); Fisher et al. (1962a)
E. coli alkaline phosphatase	8×10^4	4×10^4	2	Amino acid composition; no. tryptic peptides; N-terminal groups	Rothman and Byrne (1963)
Pig heart lipoyl dehydrogenase	10^5	5×10^4	2	Amino acid composition; no. tryptic peptides	Massey et al. (1962)
Rabbit muscle glyceraldehyde-3-phosphate dehydrogenase	$1.2–1.4 \times 10^5$	4×10^4	3–4	Complete amino acid sequence around active center	Harris et al. (1963)
Rabbit muscle aldolase	1.42×10^5	2.2×10^4	6	N-terminal groups; molecular weight	Hass (1964); Hass and Lewis (1963)
Rabbit muscle enolase	8.5×10^4	4.2×10^4	2	C-terminal and N-terminal groups	Winstead and Wold (1964)
Liver alcohol dehydrogenase	8.3×10^4	4.2×10^4	2	2 identical octapeptides (including active center) per mole enzyme	Li and Vallee (1964)

[*] For a discussion of numerous other examples in which identical subunits seem more or less probable, see Reithel (1963).

interallelic complementation in enzyme formation which is now generally accepted was first suggested by Catcheside and Overton (1958).
These authors speculated that ". . . in a B plus D heterocaryon, two
types of template B and D exist, each determining its characteristic
product, a B- or D-type polypeptide chain. It is further presumed
that one stage in the shaping of an enzyme is the aggregation of at
least two of these products. In some cases, by chance, the aggregation will involve heterologous products. Other stages in the final
shaping of the molecule are likely to involve specific folding. Presumably any one mutant has a defect which results in a fault in
folding and so in the formation of a protein sufficiently different from
the enzyme as to lack its specific activity." One way in which different mutant polypeptide chains could be complementary was thought
to be "co-operation in the direction of the process of folding in a
mixed aggregate." Catcheside went on to suggest that "the absence
of complementation (among an extensive series of mutants) could be
taken to indicate that the enzyme is shaped from a single polypeptide chain, whereas the presence of complementation indicates
the aggregation of two or more chains."

In other words, it was postulated that in cases of interallelic complementation the normal enzyme was a *homomultimer*[1] consisting
of two or more identical polypeptide chains, while the enzyme
formed by interallelic complementation was a *heteromultimer* consisting of different mutant polypeptide varieties somehow correcting
each other's tendencies towards faulty folding. Soon afterwards essentially the same suggestion was made by Fincham (1959) and by
Brenner (1959).

The hybrid protein hypothesis, as it may be called, was at first received with some skepticism because it implied that, since interallelic complementation occurred within most extensive series of
multiple alleles, many or most enzymes were multimeric in structure,
and this was not known to be true. However, during the last 5 years
this prediction of the hypothesis has been increasingly borne out.
As more and more enzymic proteins of aggregate molecular weight
of 100,000 or more are subjected to chemical analysis it begins to
look as if they are all multimers, sometimes consisting of more than
one kind of polypeptide chain but probably more often containing a
fixed number of identical chains. Dimeric enzyme proteins are quite
common, but higher multimers are also frequent, with numbers of
monomers as high as 16 or more in some cases. Table 4-1 summarizes

[1] Following Crick and Orgel (1963), the term "multimer" is preferred to
"polymer" since the latter term is usually used for linear structures with relatively small repeating units held together by covalent bonds.

TABLE 4-2 Examples of Complementation *in Vitro* between Protein Products of Allelic Mutants

Organism	Gene	Enzyme	Preparation	Conditions used for reaction*	Reference
Neurospora crassa	ad-4	Adenylosuccinase	Frozen mycelial powder or partly purified mutant proteins	Mixing in 0.05 M Tris buffer at pH 7.0; improved by successive treatments with PCMB and mercaptoethanol	Woodward (1959)
	am	NADP-linked glutamate dehydrogenase	Purified mutant proteins	Mixing in 0.05 M phosphate buffer at pH 5.8, followed by adjustment to pH 7.4 †	Fincham and Coddington (1963a)
	tryp-3	Tryptophan synthetase	Partly purified mutant proteins	Mixing in 0.05 or 0.1 M phosphate, pH 7.8, with 0.05 M EDTA, 5×10^{-6} M pyridoxal phosphate and 10^{-3} M DL-serine	Suyama (1963)
Salmonella typhimurium	his-B	Imidazole glycerol phosphate dehydrase	Crude extracts of derepressed cells	Mixing in 0.1 M triethanolamine buffer, pH 7.5, with 0.01 M mercaptoethanol and 0.001 M EDTA	Loper (1961)
Escherichia coli	p	Alkaline phosphatase	Crude extracts or purified mutant proteins	0.05 M acetate buffer at pH 4.0, followed by mixing in 0.1 M Tris, 0.007 M Mg^{++}, 0.06 M KCl, 0.004 M mercaptoethanol at pH 7.8	Schlesinger and Levinthal (1963)
	z	β-Galactosidase	Purified mutant proteins	Mixing and prolonged incubation in 0.1 M phosphate, pH 7.0, 0.1 M mercaptoethanol, 0.001 M Mg^{++}, 0.002 M Mn^{++}, 0.001 M Mg "Titriplex"	Perrin (1963)

* Abbreviations: PCMB = *p*-chloromercuribenzoate; EDTA = ethylenediaminetetraacetic acid.
† Much more efficient hybridization, though giving qualitatively similar results, is obtained by the procedure of Markert (1963) and of Chilson *et al.* (1965) involving freezing and thawing with 0.05M sodium chloride (Coddington, personal communication).

some of the clearest examples of enzymes consisting of identical multiple polypeptide chains.

In vitro complementation. If interallelic complementation occurs through interaction between already formed polypeptide chains without any cleavage or synthesis of peptide bonds, it should be possible to demonstrate similar interaction in a cell-free system in which protein synthesis is impossible. Such a demonstration has now been made in a number of cases. In fact, considerably more information is available on the mechanism of complementation in *in vitro* systems than on the *in vivo* process.

In vitro complementation has been demonstrated with cell-free mutant extracts or purified mutant proteins in at least six different cases in *Neurospora crassa* and bacteria. These are listed in Table 4-2, together with some details of the experimental procedure in each case.

There are two kinds of evidence which indicate that these *in vitro* systems have some connection with *in vivo* complementation. In the first place, those pairs of mutants which produce proteins capable of complementation *in vitro* tend to be the same pairs as complement *in vivo*. Second, the properties of active enzymes formed in the cell-free systems tend to be the same as those of the corresponding *in vivo* products.

The available data from the most completely defined *in vitro* systems (*am* in *Neurospora, z* and *p* in *E. coli*) are not very extensive, but so far as they go they are consistent with a close correspondence with the *in vivo* complementation patterns. For example, in the *Neurospora am* series of mutants, am^1 is complementary in heterokaryons with am^2, am^3, or am^{19}, whereas the latter three mutants will not complement in any combination among themselves. The isolated mutant derivative of glutamate dehydrogenase produced by am^1 will react to form active enzyme with any one of the am^2, am^3, and am^{19} mutant proteins, but of the other possible combinations, am^2 + am^3, at least, give little or no active complementation product (Fincham and Stadler, 1965; Fincham, unpublished). In the case of the *E. coli z* mutants, several pairs of mutants have been shown to complement both *in vitro* and *in vivo* (Perrin, 1963; Ullman *et al.*, 1965), though this case is of doubtful relevance to our argument since, as mentioned in the previous chapters, it may well involve intergenic rather than interallelic complementation. Among the *E. coli p* mutants, only two pairs have been tested both for complementation in heterogenotes (Garen and Garen, 1963) and in the cell-free system (Schlesinger and Levinthal, 1963), but these agreed in giving a positive result in both tests. An anomaly which appeared both in the *Neurospora am* and the *E. coli p* series was the occurrence of mutants that complemented with certain other mutants *in vivo* but individually did not produce any protein recognizable immunochemically as a mutant derivative of the normal enzyme. This applies to the mutant E15 in the *p* series (Garen and Garen, 1963) and to *am*[14] (Fincham and Stadler, 1965; Roberts and Pateman, 1964), but it is not certain whether there is a complete failure of protein formation in these cases, or a reduction in the quantity of protein produced to a low level, or the formation of a more or less normal amount of an unrecognizable protein.

Rather more extensive comparisons between *in vivo* and *in vitro* complementation patterns are available in those cases where complementation tests have been performed with crude or partially purified cell-free preparations. Loper (1961), who studied *his-B* mutants of *Salmonella typhimurium* defective in imidazoleglycerol phosphate dehydrase, found that most pairs of mutants which would complement *in vivo* (as shown by abortive transduction) would also give enzyme activity in mixed extracts. Among those complementing mutants which failed to give any *in vitro* reaction were a number, belonging to the same complementation class ("C"), which produced no material (*cross-reacting material* or CRM) which would neutralize antibodies formed against the normal enzyme. These mutants pose the same problem as the CRM-negative complementing *am* and *p* mutants mentioned earlier. No mutant pairs which did not complement *in vivo* gave any activity in mixed extracts; the same was true in Woodward's (1959) original demonstration of *in vitro* complementation with adenylosuccinase-deficient mutants of *Neurospora*.

Suyama and Bonner (1964) made an extensive survey of complementation in mixed extracts of *tryp-3* mutants of *Neurospora*, deficient in tryptophan synthetase. The extent of complementation *in vitro* was never very great in these experiments, seldom giving as much as a twofold increase in activity over what would have been expected from the mutant extracts without any interaction. However, accepting that there was a real enhancement of activity in some of their mixtures, there is no doubt of the correlation with complementing ability *in vivo*. Forty-one pairwise combinations were tested *in vitro*. Of those 15 pairs which complemented in heterokaryons, 12 were judged to give significant complementation in mixed extracts and 3 not to do so, while of the remaining 26 which did not complement in heterokaryons, 3 appeared to complement *in vitro* and 23 did not.

Turning now to comparisons between corresponding *in vitro* and *in vivo* complementation products, information is available only in a very few cases. In the *Neurospora am* series the active enzyme formed in the $am^1 + am^3$ heterokaryon is a glutamate dehydrogenase with a Michaelis constant for glutamate which is about two to three times higher than the typical wild-type value. The enzyme formed by the *in vitro* reaction of the am^1 and am^3 mutant proteins shows the same peculiarity (Fincham and Coddington, 1963b). Among the *p* mutants of *E. coli*, deficient in alkaline phosphatase, the pair U9 and S33 complement *in vivo* to form an unusually thermolabile variety of the enzyme (Garen and Garen, 1963; cf. Table 3-2). The product of the reaction of the isolated U9 and S33 proteins is also thermolabile (Schlesinger and Levinthal, 1963), though the two sets of data cannot be compared quantitatively because of a difference in the temperatures used in the inactivation experiments. Suyama and Bonner (1964) have also obtained evidence, with the *tryp-3* mutants of *Neurospora*, that the *in vitro* and *in vivo* complementation products of the same pair of alleles tend to be similar in thermostability and widely different from the wild-type enzyme in this respect. Two of the foregoing examples are illustrated in Figure 4-1.

Thus the evidence as a whole, though still rather meager, supports the idea that the *in vitro* and *in vivo* processes are similar in their products, if not necessarily in their mechanisms.

Mechanisms of hybrid protein formation in *in vitro* systems. What is happening in *in vitro* complementation systems? The simplest and clearest results are those of Schlesinger and Levinthal (1963). The alkaline phosphatase of *E. coli* has been shown by Rothman and Byrne (1963) to be a dimer composed of two subunits, each of molecular weight approximately 40,000. The subunits are almost certainly identical (cf. Table 4-1), and the enzyme contains zinc. Schlesinger and Levinthal found that the enzyme dissociated into inactive monomers either by treatment by thioglycollate and urea or, more simply, by incubation for a few minutes in acetate buffer at pH 4.0. The monomers could be clearly distinguished from dimers by their slower rate of sedimentation through a sucrose density gradient. Incubation of monomers, prepared by the pH 4 treatment, at pH 7.8 (0.1 M Tris buffer containing 10^{-4} M ZnCl$_2$) led to a time-dependent reformation of enzymically active dimer molecules. The reactivation reaction showed bimolecular kinetics. Mutant varie-

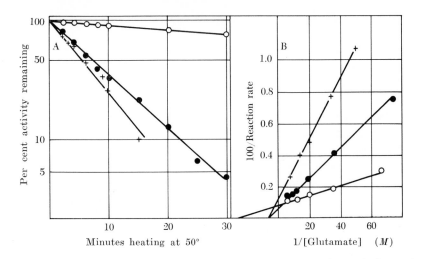

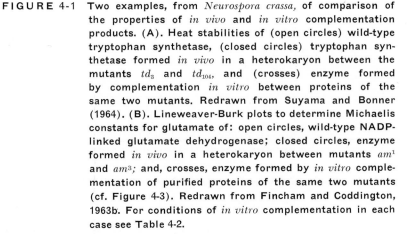

FIGURE 4-1 Two examples, from *Neurospora crassa,* of comparison of the properties of *in vivo* and *in vitro* complementation products. (A). Heat stabilities of (open circles) wild-type tryptophan synthetase, (closed circles) tryptophan synthetase formed *in vivo* in a heterokaryon between the mutants td_3 and td_{104}, and (crosses) enzyme formed by complementation *in vitro* between proteins of the same two mutants. Redrawn from Suyama and Bonner (1964). (B). Lineweaver-Burk plots to determine Michaelis constants for glutamate of: open circles, wild-type NADP-linked glutamate dehydrogenase; closed circles, enzyme formed *in vivo* in a heterokaryon between mutants am^1 and am^3; and, crosses, enzyme formed by *in vitro* complementation of purified proteins of the same two mutants (cf. Figure 4-3). Redrawn from Fincham and Coddington, 1963b. For conditions of *in vitro* complementation in each case see Table 4-2.

ties of the enzyme, purified from mutants U9 and S33, could also be dissociated into monomers by treatment at pH 4.0. Incubation of mixed U9 and S33 monomers at pH 7.8 in the Tris-ZnCl₂ buffer led to a time-dependent formation of enzyme activity more than 10 times greater, in terms of the amount of protein present, than would have been given by either of the slightly active mutant proteins by itself. All the activity resembled the normal enzyme in its rate of sedimentation through a sucrose density gradient, and thus was due to dimer molecules (Figure 4-2).

The conclusion that the active dimers were hybrids, each contain-

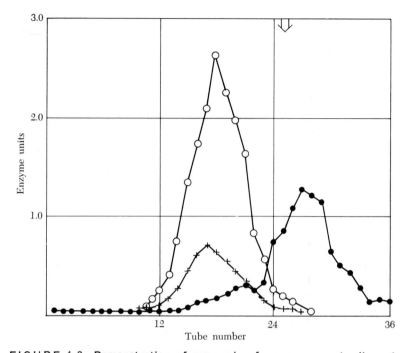

FIGURE 4-2   Demonstration of conversion from monomer to dimer in the *in vitro* formation of alkaline phosphatase from mutant proteins in *E. coli*. Enzyme units (E.U.) are plotted against tube number of samples collected from sucrose density gradients after ultracentrifugation. Tube 1 corresponds to the bottom of the tube, and tube 36 to the top. Results of three experiments are superimposed. Open circles: wild-type enzyme (dimer). Closed circles: mutant S33 acid-prepared monomer, assayed by *in vitro* complementation of the tube contents with U9 monomer. Crosses: U9-S33 complementation product formed by interaction between monomers. The broad arrow indicates the position of radioactive reduced and alkylated wild-type enzyme, used as a marker for the position of monomers. After Schlesinger and Levinthal (1963).

ing one U9 and one S33 monomer, was strongly supported by the observation that, after electrophoresis in starch gel, they showed a series of isozymic bands intermediate in position between those of the electrophoretically different U9 and S33 proteins. Furthermore, the yield of active product varies with the ratio of the two interacting proteins as if its formation depended on the association of one monomer of each kind in each active molecule.

It was possible to calculate the specific activity of the active hybrids on the assumption, which was consistent with the data on the extent of complementation as a function of the relative proportions of the monomers, that monomers associated at random. For example, given a one-to-one ratio of the two kinds of monomers, one would obtain 50% hybrids and 25% each of the two unmixed dimers if this assumption were true. The calculation led to the conclusion that the hybrid dimer molecules had 5% of the activity of wild-type enzyme. However, the fact that the same pair of mutants complement *in vivo* to give up to 20% of the wild-type level of activity (Garen and Garen, 1963, cf. Table 3-2) suggests that the hybrid dimers may, in fact, be more active than this, which would in turn imply that the yield of such dimers in the *in vitro* system is not as great as one would expect from random association of monomers.

Schlesinger and Levinthal's study is the only one on *in vitro* complementation which provides a clear mechanism for the formation of hybrid protein molecules. It seems fully established in this case that hybrid formation is brought about by dissociation into monomers, followed by reassociation.

The process of complementation between mutant glutamate dehydrogenase varieties, formed by various *am* mutants of *Neurospora,* is in some ways more puzzling than the example just considered since there is no indication as to how hybrid protein is formed in the *in vitro* system. The NADP-linked glutamate dehydrogenase (GDH) of *Neurospora* is a large protein of about 260,-000 to 270,000 molecular weight, and the amino acid composition, taken together with the number of peptides obtained after digestion with trypsin, suggests that this is made up of 8 or possibly 10 identical subunits (Fincham and Coddington, unpublished; Barratt, 1961). About 6 to 8 molecules of $NADPH_2$ are bound per mole of enzyme (Fincham, unpublished).

Of the mutants which show *in vivo* complementation all except one (am^{14}) produce mutant forms of GDH which can be purified by the same fractionation procedure as is effective in the wild type (Fincham and Stadler, 1964). These mutant proteins all have sedimentation coefficients similar to that of the wild-type enzyme, and thus they are probably all similar-sized aggregates. Of the protein-forming mutants, the combinations $am^1 + am^2$, $am^1 + am^3$, and $am^1 + am^{19}$ will complement in heterokaryons and the corresponding pairs of mutant proteins will do so in the *in vitro* system (cf. Table 4–2) (Fincham and Coddington, 1963a, b; and see pp. 7, 88). The same procedure worked for all three pairs of proteins. The protein mixture, originally in 0.05 M phosphate buffer at pH 7.4, was adjusted to pH 5.8 with acetic acid and then readjusted to pH 7.4 with sodium hydroxide. The reaction at pH 5.8 was evidently very rapid and no time dependence could be convincingly demonstrated. The readjustment to pH 7.4 was essential for the appearance of activity, which, again, appeared to be almost instantaneous. While a pH of around 5.8 was optimal for the complementation reaction, some activity resulted from a treatment at pH 6.5 and even at moderately alkaline pH, such as pH 9. However, no reaction appeared to occur in the original phosphate buffer at pH 7.4.

An obvious possibility, especially in the light of the studies on complementation in the *Escherichia coli* alkaline phosphatase system, was that dissociation into subunits was occurring at pH 5.8, followed by reassociation with consequent hybrid formation at pH 7.4. If this were the case, one would expect to be able to detect a change in the sedimentation characteristics of the proteins with pH alteration. Surprisingly, no significant decrease in sedimentation coefficient, such as might have been expected to follow from a dissociation into subunits, could be detected at pH 5.8; if anything, there was a slight *increase* in sedimentation rate at this pH (Fincham and Coddington, 1963a). A more detailed study of the sedimentation characteristics of the am^3 protein (Coddington, 1963) over a wide range of concentration showed a small linear increase in S value with increasing dilution, with no indication of dissociation into subunits even at the highest dilutions at either pH 5.8 or at pH 7.4. Following readjustment of the pH of the complementing mixture from 5.8 to 7.4, there was again no significant change in S value; the protein, which now had up to about 10% of the specific enzyme activity of wild-type GDH, still appeared homogeneous in the ultracentrifuge and closely similar to normal GDH in S value. These observations did not rule out the mechanism of dissociation-reassociation, since a small number of subunits could be in equilibrium with a large number of multimers, but they certainly lent it no support. As an alternative hypothesis it was suggested that aggregate protein molecules might exchange subunits on contact, without the subunits ever being free in solution. Contacts at pH 5.8, relatively close to the isoelectric point of the protein, would probably be much more frequent than at pH 7.4. The slower reaction at alkaline pH may well be dependent on a different mechanism.

In view of the uncertainty as to mechanism, it became all the more important to demonstrate that the enzyme activity appearing in the *in vitro* system really was due to hybrid formation. The

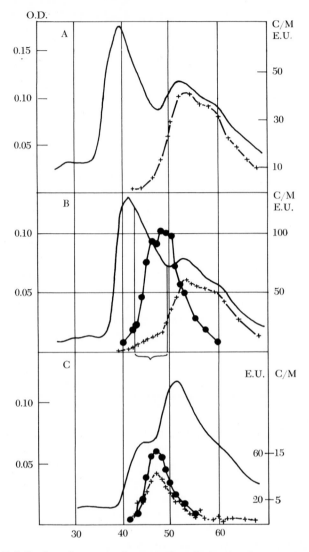

FIGURE 4-3   *In vitro* complementation between two mutant forms
(am^1 and am^3) of *Neurospora* glutamate dehydrogenase; and
demonstration that am^1 protein is incorporated into the
active product. A: mixture of am^3 and ^{35}S-labeled am^1
protein fractionated on a DEAE-cellulose column. B:
same mixture after complementation reaction. C: selected
fractions taken from B (as indicated by bracketed vertical
lines) and refractionated together with an excess of nonradioactive am^1 protein. Continuous full line: absorbancy
(O.D.) at 280 mμ, indicating protein. Crosses: radioactive

mutant pair $am^1 + am^3$ provided a favorable system for analysis since the am^1 and am^3 proteins can be separated from each other on a column of diethylaminoethyl (DEAE-) cellulose, am^3 protein being eluted from the column at a lower salt concentration. Using a gradient of phosphate concentration, a mixture of the two proteins, made at pH 7.4, can be almost completely resolved into its components. Following the *in vitro* hybridization procedure, the new enzyme activity formed a well-defined peak in the elution pattern midway between the peaks formed by the unchanged am^1 and am^3 proteins. The degree of resolution of the components of the mixture was not, however, adequate to show really convincingly that material from both am^1 and am^3 peaks had contributed to the complementation product. The necessary demonstration was obtained through experiments in which first one and then the other mutant protein was labeled with ^{35}S by growing the appropriate mutant strain on medium containing radioactive sulfate. Some of the results are summarized by Figure 4-3. It was clear that the enzymically active product, which constituted no more than 5–10% of the reaction mixture, did incorporate material from both reacting proteins. Furthermore, since the specific radioactivity of the labeled protein used in each experiment was known, it was possible to calculate the specific enzyme activity of the complementation product in terms of each component in turn. The two specific activities turned out to be nearly the same, and approaching the value characteristic of wild-type GDH. Thus the conclusion was drawn that the hybrid formed, at least under the conditions of these experiments, contained, overall, subunits of the two mutant types in equal proportion and had about half of the specific activity of the wild-type enzyme (Coddington and Fincham, 1965). In the same paper it was shown, by sedimentation analysis using sucrose density gradients, that the complementation product was identical in S value to wild-type GDH and thus probably had, at least on average, 4 am^1 and 4 am^3 polypeptide chains (assuming that the enzyme normally contains 8 identical chains). For reasons to be outlined later, it seems likely that hybrid

---

counts per min. (C/M). Closed circles: enzyme units (E.U.) formed by complementation. The size of the samples taken for radioactive counting was not the same for the three columns. In a second experiment with labeled am^3 and unlabeled am^1 protein the incorporation of am^3 protein into the active product was also shown. After Coddington and Fincham (1965).

molecules containing unequal proportions of the two kinds of chain can be formed, especially when very unequal proportions of the two mutant proteins are used in the reaction mixture.

To summarize, it seems in this case that normal-sized mixed multimers can be formed by interaction between normal-sized un-mixed multimers, but there is no indication that free subunits are involved in the reaction. It is possible that some kind of exchange of polypeptide subunits can occur between aggregates without the subunits ever being free in solution.

Mechanisms of hybrid formation *in vivo.* There is ample evidence that hybrid proteins are commonly formed in heteroallelic diploids (see also Chapter 6), and some evidence, reviewed earlier, that similar hybrids can be formed by protein-protein interaction *in vitro.* It does not follow, however, that *in vitro* and *in vivo* mechanisms are the same. Indeed, when two kinds of mutant polypeptide chains are being produced together in the same cell one tends to suppose that hybrid multimers are formed directly from monomers, without any necessity for unmixed multimers to be formed first. This supposition depends to some extent on the assumption that polypeptide chains are released from the ribosomal complexes where they are synthesized before undergoing aggregation. Some observations of Zipser and Perrin on *E. coli* β-galactosidase are relevant in this connection. As already mentioned (pp. 42–43) β-galactosidase contains identical subunits even though the latter seem to consist of nonidentical chains, and so the way in which the full aggregate is formed is of interest in connection with multimeric proteins generally. Zipser (1963b) found that in wild-type *E. coli* an appreciable amount of active β-galactosidase occurred bound to the ribosomes. This bound enzyme could be recovered quantitatively in soluble form by treatment with sodium dodecyl sulfate (SDS), and it was found to consist of molecules of the usual size. Since experiments on the kinetics of enzyme induction by lactose indicated that the ribosome-bound fraction was a precursor of free enzyme, the presence of fully assembled multimers on the ribosomes presented a problem.[2] Did they get there as a result of synthesis, either in succession or simultaneously, of all the chains on the same ribosome complex containing, according to current ideas, only one molecule of messenger RNA? Or was, perhaps, only one of the chains actually made at the site at which it was bound, the others being "picked up" from the solution?

---

[2] Schwartz's (1962) observation of hybrid esterase bound to the particulate fraction in extracts of heterozygous maize poses a similar problem.

Zipser and Perrin's (1963) observations on *in vitro* complementation provided a model for the latter alternative. While the mutant z_{178} formed no more than a trace of β-galactosidase activity in any cellular fraction, the complementary mutant z_1 had significant activity associated with the ribosomes, though almost none in the soluble fraction. The z_1/z_{178} heterogenote had much more activity, with as much as a half of it bound to the ribosomes compared with less than 1% bound to ribosomes in wild-type cells (Table 4-3). Furthermore, z_1 soluble protein was found to complement *in vitro* with z_{178} ribosomes, the reaction being considerably faster than that involving free z_{178} protein. On the other hand, z_1 ribosomes complemented very slowly or not at all with free z_{178} protein (Table 4-3).

One can interpret this situation by saying that z_1 protein cannot

TABLE 4-3 Complementation on Ribosomes, *in Vitro* and *in Vivo*, Leading to β-Galactosidase Formation in *E. coli* *

	A. In vivo		
E. coli strain	**Total enzyme (as % of wild)**	**Ribosome-bound enzyme (as % of wild)**	**Ribosome-bound enzyme (as % of total)**
Wild	100	100	0.66
z_{178}	Trace	Trace	—
z_1	0.11	6.6	37
$z_{178}/F'z_1$ heterogenote	4.6	398	53

	B. In vitro †	
Ribosomes from	**Mutant protein from**	**Ribosome-bound enzyme (as % of wild)**
Wild	None	100
Wild	z_1	102
Wild	z_{178}	98
z_{178}	None	0.22
z_{178}	z_1	92
z_{178}	z_{178}	0.21
z_1	None	6.6
z_1	z_1	6.5
z_1	z_{178}	6.6

* Data of Zipser and Perrin, 1963.
† Ribosomes and purified mutant proteins, each at about 5 mg/ml, were incubated in 0.01 M Tris, 0.01 M Mg acetate at pH 7.3 for 30 min at 25°C.

readily form aggregates of full size except in association with ribosomes, and that z_{178} protein cannot form active aggregates at all by itself, but can do so in association with z_1 protein on ribosomes. The reason why z_1 ribosomes do not complement appreciably with free z_{178} protein may be that they are already saturated with poorly active z_1 aggregates; the z_{178} ribosomes, on the other hand, may carry single subunits of z_{178} protein capable of reacting readily with free or partially aggregated z_1 subunits.

Whether this situation can serve as a useful general model for complementation *in vivo* is doubtful, but it does at least suggest that the ease with which polypeptide chains can interact to form aggregates is very much dependent on their conformation, and that this in turn can be strongly affected by association with ribosomes.

Why does hybridization lead to activity? — The conformation-correction hypothesis. When a heteromultimer composed of two somewhat different polypeptide chains has more activity than either type of homomultimer, one can describe the situation formally by saying that each type of chain provides some component of the enzymically active structure which the other lacks. One explanation could be that the active center of the enzyme required two different chemical groups supplied by nearby regions of different chains. To give one of the simplest models, one can imagine that homologous regions of different chains are aligned in reversed sequence, so that group X of chain A is adjacent to group Y of chain B, and group Y of chain A to group X of chain B (Figure 4-4). The juxtaposition of an X and a Y is assumed to be necessary and sufficient for enzyme activity. In the case of the wild-type enzyme two chains would form two such active centers, while if X is defective in chain A and Y defective in chain B there would nevertheless still be one functional active center. The heterodimer would thus show complementation with, perhaps, 50% of the specific activity of wild-type enzyme, while neither kind of unmixed mutant dimer would have any activity at all. This seems a reasonable model which may be true in some cases, but as yet too little is known of the detailed chemistry of complementing proteins to say how commonly applicable it is. It has the weakness that it is difficult to imagine how it could explain rather numerous mutually complementing classes of allelic mutants such as are quite often found (see the next chapter). One would expect only as many complementation groups as there were essential groups in the enzyme active center capable of being lost independently by mutation.

An alternative idea is that the appearance of activity in a hybrid

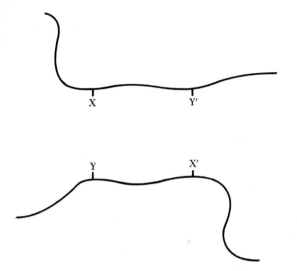

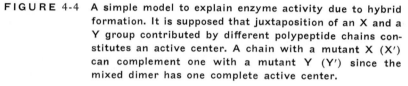

FIGURE 4-4   A simple model to explain enzyme activity due to hybrid
            formation. It is supposed that juxtaposition of an X and a
            Y group contributed by different polypeptide chains con-
            stitutes an active center. A chain with a mutant X (X')
            can complement one with a mutant Y (Y') since the
            mixed dimer has one complete active center.

enzyme is due to an effect on the *conformation* of one kind of chain
by the other. This is essentially the explanation first proposed by
Catcheside (cf. p. 67), and it has been discussed in a more detailed and explicit fashion by Crick and Orgel (1964). The geometrical aspects of the conformation-correction hypothesis are considered in the next chapter. Here we will consider the evidence (1)
that complex proteins can exist in alternative conformations which
may be stable under some conditions and readily interconvertible
under others, and (2) that mutant enzymes are often inactive as a
result of their abnormal conformation, and that this can sometimes
be corrected by hybridization with another mutant enzyme with a
different defect.

Conformational changes in enzymes have been given much attention during the last few years, largely because of the importance
given to such changes in Monod's theory of *allostery* (Monod,
Changeux, and Jacob, 1963). Briefly, an allosteric enzyme is defined
as one which can combine specifically with a substance sterically
unrelated to the substrate at a site different from the substrate
binding site and, as a result, undergo a conformational change or

allosteric transition. The compound (the *allosteric effector*) which brings about the conformational change is often the end product of the metabolic pathway of which the enzyme forms a part, and in such cases the allosteric transition is such as to inhibit enzyme activity. The allosteric effect thus serves to regulate the supply of end product of the pathway. It may or may not be accompanied by a change in the state of aggregation of the enzyme concerned. Without attempting a detailed review of the evidence for the allosteric model, one can say that the specific inhibitory effect of an end product, combining at a site other than the substrate site, is an observed fact in a number of instances, and that the conjecture that this inhibition is due to an induced change in conformation, while less well substantiated, seems highly plausible. Koshland (1960) has held for a number of years that combination of an enzyme with substrate molecules is very generally accompanied by conformational changes, and evidence has been accumulating in favor of this view, the conformational changes being detectable by optical and other physicochemical measurements (e.g., Labouesse, Hairsteen, and Hess, 1962; Czerlinski and Schreck, 1964).

A number of examples are also known of proteins being reversibly interconverted between two or more conformations by shifts in pH value, ionic strength, or temperature. A particularly good example is yeast enolase, which is converted to an inactive form by reduction of the pH to below 5.5 and can be reactivated by restoring the pH to neutrality. The exact pH at which the transition occurs depends on temperature, lower temperatures favoring activation (Westhead, 1964; Rosenberg and Lumry, 1964). In this case the transconformation appears to involve no change in the degree of aggregation of the enzyme, though the inactive form appears to be partly unfolded and therefore less compact than the active enzyme. Other examples of temperature-dependent transconformations in enzymes have been described by Dua and Burris (1963) and Hayashi, Hamaguchi, and Funatsu (1963).

However, most normal enzymes, apart from allosteric transitions which have an obvious functional significance, seem to have conformations which are quite stable under any conditions that might be thought to approximate the physiological norm. This, no doubt, is due not to any property of proteins as such, but to natural selection of stable structures. Newly arising mutant enzymes, on the other hand, have not been subjected to natural selection and it is not surprising to find among them various kinds of conformational instability. Some of the best examples are provided by the *am* mutants of *Neurospora crassa*, which produce altered forms of glutamate dehydrogenase.

Two classes of conformationally abnormal varieties of glutamate dehydrogenase are found among the *am* mutants. The first class, exemplified by am^2, am^3, and am^{19}, which are all auxotrophic mutants, are relatively stable but in an abnormal and inactive conformation. The second class, found in prototrophic secondary mutant derivatives of the three mutants just mentioned, are rather delicately balanced between active conformationally normal and inactive conformationally abnormal forms, and can be converted from one to the other by quite small changes in the temperature, pH, or ionic composition of the solvent. All these conformationally abnormal enzyme varieties can be activated under appropriate conditions. Their properties are summarized in Table 4-4.

The evidence that the changes involved are conformational in character, and do not involve the reversible binding of inhibitor or activator molecules, is clearest in the cases of the am^{21} and am^{R24} proteins. In the former mutant, the purified protein can be converted very readily from the inactive to the active form and back again by quite small adjustments in temperature or pH value. At 22°C the enzyme is almost inactive at pH 8.0 but predominantly active at pH 8.5. At pH 8.0 it is active at 30°C (Fincham, 1957; Fincham and Garner, unpublished). The active and inactive forms of this mutant enzyme do not differ appreciably from each other or from wild-type enzyme in S value (Fincham, unpublished). Furthermore, both the activation and inactivation reactions appear to be first order (Fincham, 1957). There seems little doubt that we are here dealing with a conformational change in the protein without any change in degree of aggregation.

In the case of am^{R24}, obtained as a secondary mutant from am^{19}, the enzyme is activated by dicarboxylate or polycarboxylate ions in the concentration range 10^{-2}–10^{-1} M. Either succinate or ethylenediaminetetraacetate is effective in bringing about activation (Sundaram and Fincham, 1964). Succinate is not bound to the activated enzyme but merely catalyzes its formation, as shown by an experiment in which ^{14}C-succinate was used as activator and then removed from the protein by means of a Sephadex dextran column without any immediate loss in enzyme activity. As in the case of am^{21} protein, the active and inactive forms are similar to each other and to wild-type enzyme in sedimentation properties. The am^{R24} protein is especially interesting because the inactive conformation is electrophoretically abnormal, running about 8 to 10% faster at pH

TABLE 4-4   Properties of Mutant Varieties of *Neurospora* NAPA-Linked GDH Interconvertible between Active and Inactive Forms *

Mutant†	Origin	Conditions for activation‡	Whether active *in vivo*	Other properties different from wild enzyme
am²	Wild	High conc. (ca. 0.1 *M*) polycarboxylate ions; 35°C; pH > 8.4	No	Highly thermolabile
am³	Wild	High conc. (ca. 0.1 *M*) polycarboxylate ions; 35°C; pH > 8.4	No	Separable from wild enzyme on DEAE-cellulose
am¹⁹	Wild	High conc. (ca. 0.1 *M*) polycarboxylate ions; 35°C; pH > 8.4 (very slow activation)	No	Inactive form more negatively charged than wild enzyme
am²¹	*am²*	pH > 8.3 at 20°, or temp. > 27° at pH 8.0	Yes	Highly thermolabile
am^{R24}	*am¹⁹*	Like *am¹⁹*, but activation very rapid	Yes	Inactive form more negatively charged than wild enzyme
am³ᵇ	*am³*	Incubation with α-oxoglutarate + NADPH₂	Yes	—
am³⁻⁵⁰	*am³*	Presence of ethylenediaminetetraacetate, 0.01 *M* or more	Yes	—

* All the enzyme varieties listed are wholly or predominantly in inactive forms at 20–25°C in 0.05 *M* phosphate at pH 8.0.

† References: *am²*, Fincham (1962); *am³*, Fincham (1962) and Roberts (1964); *am^{R24}* and *am¹⁹*, Sundaram and Fincham (1964); *am²¹*, Fincham (1957) and Garner and Fincham (in preparation); *am³ᵇ*, Fincham (1962); *am³⁻⁵⁰*, Pateman and Fincham (1965).

‡ The optimum conditions and rates of activation differ somewhat between *am²*, *am³*, and *am¹⁹*. Not all the possible procedures have been tried on all mutant enzymes; for instance, some of the procedures effective on *am³*, etc., may well work for *am³ᵇ* and *am³⁻⁵⁰* as well, but the procedures mentioned for the latter varieties are not effective on *am³* enzyme.

8.7 than the normal enzyme. Activation is accompanied by a normalization of electrophoretic mobility. Since *am^{R24}* grows normally on unsupplemented medium, the enzyme is presumably wholly or partly in the active form in the intact mycelium; both forms are present in fresh dilute phosphate buffer extracts but the active form is very unstable under these conditions.

The inactive protein produced by the primary mutant am^{19} turned out to be rather similar to the R24 enzyme in properties, being activated by the same procedure and showing a similar electrophoretic shift. However, activation proceeded much more slowly in the am^{19} protein, and it seems that the inactive conformation is much more stable relative to the active one in this case. The effect of the second mutation in am^{R24} is evidently to shift the equilibrium in favor of the active conformation.

The other mutant enzyme varieties listed in Table 4-4 may also, by analogy, be regarded as examples of rather similar kinds of conformational instability.

The relevance of these mutants to the theory of complementation arises from the fact that, with the exception of am^{3-50}, they all complement in heterokaryons with am^1 to form enzyme with relatively normal properties (Fincham and Stadler, 1965; Pateman and Fincham, 1965). The latter mutant produces a protein which, although similar to wild-type GDH in all known physical and chemical properties, has no enzyme activity under any known conditions. As was discussed in detail in the previous section, am^1 protein will complement in vitro with am^3 protein with the formation of an active hybrid, and in vitro complementation has also been demonstrated between am^1 and am^2, am^{19} and am^{R24} proteins respectively (Fincham and Coddington, 1963b; Sundaram and Fincham, 1964). In the case of the $am^1 + am^3$ hybrid product, the specific enzyme activity is approximately what one would expect if the am^3 component of the hybrid were fully activated. The obvious inference is that the activity of the hybrid multimer is due to a correction of the conformation of the am^3 chains so that their potential activity becomes stabilized, no longer requiring a special ionic environment. It seems reasonable to suppose that in a closely packed aggregate of symmetrically arranged subunits all the subunits have to have the same conformation. Thus in a mixed multimer containing two kinds of mutant chain, each tending towards a different conformation, the aggregate as a whole has, on this view, to choose one conformation or the other. If the am^1 protein resembles wild-type GDH in being conformationally very stable, in spite of having lost something essential for activity, the presence of am^1 subunits will tend to force the hybrid toward a normal conformation. The idea is illustrated in Figure 4-5.

Rather more direct evidence in support of this picture is available from the $am^1 + am^{19}$ in vitro complementation system. Here, as has already been mentioned, the am^{19} protein is electrophoretically

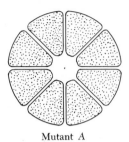

Mutant *A*

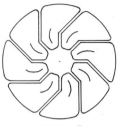

Mutant *B*

Hybrids

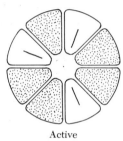

Active

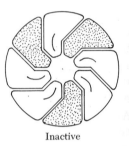

Inactive

FIGURE 4-5   A model for complementation by conformational correction. The protein is supposed to be an octomer with
subunits arranged, for simplicity of representation, in a
two-dimensional radially symmetrical array. Mutant A
produces a protein which is conformationally normal but
with no complete enzymically active center. Mutant B
protein has a potential active center (symbolized by
curved line in each subunit) but is inactive because of a
conformational abnormality. Hybrids may, depending on
the proportions of the two subunits, have either type of
conformation. Subunits of mutant B protein, when present in conformationally normal hybrids, have a functional
active center (symbolized by a straight line in each
subunit).

abnormal in its inactive conformation. When it is activated it
becomes electrophoretically normal. We can take its electrophoretic
properties as an index of conformational normality or abnormality.
Thus it seems very significant that the active complementation
product formed either by *in vivo* or *in vitro* complementation of *am¹*
and *am¹⁹* is indistinguishable electrophoretically from *am¹* protein
or wild-type GDH. The complementation product would seem,
therefore, to be conformationally normal, as if the faulty conforma-

tion of the am^{19} component had been corrected as a result of hybridization. A further significant fact is that as one adds more and more am^{19} protein to a constant amount of am^{1}, the yield of active product reaches an optimum at not much more than a one-to-one ratio of the two proteins, and thereafter declines to a lower value (Figure 4-6). At the same time, the enzymic properties of the product change progressively, taking on more of the character of mutant protein as shown by enhanced activity in a system containing a high concentration of carboxylate ions (glutamate in this case) (Figure 4-6). Electrophoretic analysis shows that some of the conformationally normal component disappears as a large excess of am^{19} protein is added. The most reasonable conclusion is that more than one kind of hybrid is possible (a conclusion also reached in the case of the $am^{1} + am^{2}$ system; Fincham and Coddington, 1963b) and that hybrid multimers with an excess of am^{19} chains tend towards the am^{19} conformation and are consequently inactive or active only after some degree of activating treatment.[1]

The same general hypothesis suggests a speculative explanation for the otherwise puzzling case of am^{14} (see p. 70), which appears to produce no mutant protein variety and yet complements several other mutants. It may be that the conformation which am^{14} chains tend to assume is so abnormal as to be incompatible with stable multimer formation. Thus am^{14} by itself might produce no protein recognizable as related to normal GDH. Nevertheless, am^{14} chains might be able to participate in the formation of reasonably stable *mixed* aggregates with mutant protein of other kinds, and once formed into such aggregates they might be active enzymically.

Whether the correction of conformation hypothesis will turn out to apply to most examples of complementation remains to be seen. There is at present very little evidence bearing directly on this question. Some indirect evidence, however, comes from the study of complementation maps, which are considered in the following chapter.

Negative complementation. If, as suggested in the foregoing argument and in Figure 4-5, a conformationally abnormal protein subunit can sometimes impose its faulty conformation in a mixed aggregate, one would expect sometimes to find one allele actually interfering with the formation of an active protein by another. Thus a pair of mutants might interact to form an enzyme less active or

---

[1] For further evidence for this interpretation see Coddington, Fincham, and Sundaram (in preparation).

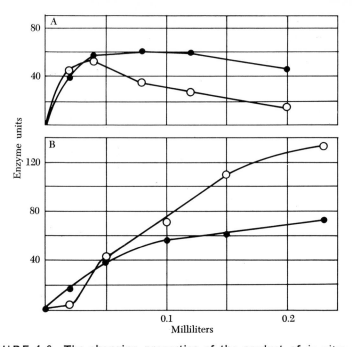

FIGURE 4-6   The changing properties of the product of *in vitro* complementation between *am¹* and *am¹⁹* mutant varieties of glutamate dehydrogenase in *Neurospora*. In A, 0.06 ml of *am¹* protein solution was mixed with different volumes of *am¹⁹* protein solution in a total volume of 0.25 ml. In B, 0.02 ml of *am¹⁹* solution was mixed with different volumes of *am¹* solution in a total of 0.25 ml. Both solutions contained about 0.4 mg/ml of purified protein; conditions of complementation were as given in Table 4-2; 0.1-ml samples were assayed in two systems at 35°C. Open circles: α-oxoglutarate + ammonium chloride + NADPH₂ in Tris buffer at pH 8.5, with the enzyme as the final addition to the mixture (System A of Fincham, 1962). Closed circles: 0.14 *M* L-glutamate + NADP in Tris at pH 8.5, with the enzyme incubated with the Tris-glutamate for 2 min before addition of the NADP (System C of Fincham, 1962). The wild-type enzyme gives a system A/System C activity ratio of about 2.5.

more abnormal in properties than the enzyme which would have been formed by one of the alleles by itself. This may be termed *negative complementation*. Indications of such an effect are occasionally found. For example, in *Neurospora* there is some evidence that the allele *am⁴*, which produces an inactive and very unstable derivative of glutamate dehydrogenase, interacts negatively with am^{21}, which by itself produces an active but rather labile form of the enzyme (Fincham, 1958). Possible cases of negative complementation have also been observed in bacteriophage T4 (Edgar, personal communication, and cf. Table 3-3).

In the same way, a mutant allele producing an abnormal protein might interfere with the formation of a normal product by the wild-type gene. Such an effect has not often been looked for, but evidence for it was obtained by Garen and Garen (1963) in their studies of p mutants of *E. coli* (see p. 48). They tested 8 F' strains, each one carrying a different p mutant allele in the chromosome and a wild-type p^+ gene on the episome. In four of these the alkaline phosphatase produced was found to be distinctly less stable to heating than the normal enzyme. In each of these four cases the p mutant was one which produced abnormal alkaline phosphatase protein; in one of them (S6) this protein had appreciable enzyme activity by itself. Of the pair of mutants used by Schlesinger and Levinthal (1963) in the experiment illustrated in Figure 4-2, S33 appeared to be capable of modifying the heat stability of the wild-type protein whereas U9 did not.

This kind of negative interaction, if sufficiently strong, could result in dominance of a defective mutant allele over the wild type, both in the gross phenotype as expressed in growth properties and at the level of enzyme activity. Anything like complete dominance could, however, be expected only if the function of the aggregate protein was extraordinarily sensitive to the replacement of some of its normal subunits by mutant ones.

5

COMPLEMENTATION MAPS AND

THEIR INTERPRETATION

In spite of the fact that interallelic complementation went un-recognized for so long it seems to occur in most series of alleles in *Neurospora* and at least in many series in bacteria. So wide-spread, indeed, is the phenomenon that it is important to establish whether there are *any* genes within which it does not occur.

5-1 THE GENERAL INCIDENCE OF COMPLEMENTATION

The hybrid protein hypothesis predicts that genes determining monomeric proteins should not show interallelic complementation. Only a few enzymes, of which pancreatic ribonuclease is the best known, are known for certain to consist of only a single polypeptide chain. The only monomeric protein for which a series of genetic mutants is available is the A protein component of *Escherichia coli* tryptophan synthetase. A large number of mutants producing ab-normal and, in many cases, chemically defined varieties of the pro-tein have been isolated; no evidence exists that any pair of them can show complementation, but perhaps such evidence has not been much sought for. If complementation were found among the A protein mutants it would demonstrate the inadequacy of the hybrid protein hypothesis. So long as this hypothesis continues to stand an absence of interallelic complementation is suggestive of a monomeric protein gene product.

There are, in fact, a number of loci in microorganisms at which complementation has not been found. In *Schizosaccharomyces pombe* Leupold and Gutz (1965) found no complementation among over 200 ultraviolet light- and nitrous acid-induced mutants of the *ad-7* series. Several examples were cited in Neurospora by Catcheside and Overton (1958) and Catcheside (1960).[1] The strongest case was that of *hist-6*, which showed no complementation among 99 independently isolated mutants. In *Salmonella typhimurium* Hartman, Hartman, and Serman (1960) detected complementation in 3 out of 8 genes of the *histidine* operon and no complementation in the others, but the number of different combinations tested in each case was not large.

Negative evidence from a limited number of tests should always be treated with caution. In several cases where complementation does occur the removal of only a few mutants out of a large number would leave no complementary pairs. Even if the gene in question does correspond to a multimeric protein, complementing mutants need to have special qualities—probably, in general, the ability to make a protein sufficiently abnormal to give a mutant phenotype but not so abnormal as to be incapable of correction in a hybrid multimer. These requirements may be met by only a small minority of mutants in some gene-protein systems, and some procedures for mutant isolation may miss the complementing mutants completely.

The *ad-3B* mutants of *Neurospora* are a case in point. Among 151 mutants of this series, either occurring spontaneously or induced by radiation, only 18 showed complementation. It was only following induction of mutants with the adenine analogue 2-amino-purine that complementing mutants were frequent (Brockman and De Serres, 1963; De Serres, 1963). A high proportion of the complementing strains were "leaky" mutants, that is, mutants which grew slightly on minimal medium without adenine supplement. These leaky mutants probably each produce a very slightly abnormal protein capable of more or less full enzymic activity after hybridization, and it may be that only relatively few genetic sites, some of which are especially susceptible to mutation with 2-aminopurine, are capable of mutating to give such a protein. To the extent that complementing mutants tend to be "leaky," they are quite likely to

[1] See also De Serres (1960).

be missed by selection procedures designed for the isolation of auxotrophs.

Especially relevant here are the studies of conditional lethal mutants of bacteriophage T4 made by Edgar and his colleagues (Edgar, Denhardt, and Epstein, 1964; Bernstein, Denhardt, and Edgar, 1965). Two kinds of conditional lethals were isolated. The *amber* mutants were selected for inability to grow on *E. coli* strain B while remaining capable of growth in strain CR63. These mutants, which seem to occur within most of the genes of the T4 genome, are thought to carry mutant genetic coding units which are "nonsense" in the B cell but which can be translated into some sort of acceptable sense in the CR63 cell. If in strain B they produce *no* protein corresponding to the mutant gene, they should not show intragenic complementation and, in fact, none of them do. A second group of conditional lethals were the *temperature-sensitive (ts)* mutants, which are able to form plaques at 25°C but not at 42°C. So far as the evidence goes (Epstein *et al.*, 1963) these mutants seem to form mutant proteins which are heat sensitive, but perfectly functional at the lower temperature. Like the *amber* mutants, the *ts* mutants occur throughout the genome. In striking contrast to the *amber* mutants, however, they show some degree of complementation in practically all combinations, intragenic as well as intergenic, though the yield of phage from intragenic complementation is often very low.

No doubt this is an extreme case, but it does illustrate how particular systems for selection of mutants may select for particular complementation properties. It is worth noting in parentheses that a parallel situation occurs in yeast, where mutants which are phenotypically reparable by "super-suppressor" mutations do not complement, and are probably "nonsense" mutations, whereas others which are reparable by high osmotic pressure do tend to complement and are interpreted as "mis-sense" mutations (Hawthorne and Friis, 1964). We shall return to the *ts* mutants of T4 later in this chapter.

5-2 HOW ABSOLUTE ARE THE RESULTS OF COMPLEMENTATION TESTS?

The difficulty of making a case for the absence of interallelic complementation in any particular gene is increased by the fact that the distinction between a positive and a negative complementation test is, in any case, a somewhat arbitrary one. Interallelic complementation seems seldom or never to be complete, in the sense of resulting in a normal level of a normal protein product, though it may appear to be so from growth tests. One may expect a complete range of degrees of complementation from something superficially resembling the wild phenotype down to something barely better than one of the mutants by itself. Whether slight complementation is detected depends on the sensitivity of the test, and it is likely that many allelic pairs recorded as noncomplementary do in fact complement at a very low level.

This point is well made by the results of Bernstein, Denhardt, and Edgar (1965) on temperature-sensitive (ts) mutants of bacteriophage T4. Here the test for complementation is extremely sensitive. Whereas infection of E. coli with wild-type T4 under standard conditions gives a burst size of between 100 and 300 phage particles per bacterial cell, burst sizes of as low as 0.01 per cell can be measured in a large population. Many ts mutants give burst sizes at 42°C of the order of 0.01–0.1 in single infection, but nevertheless increases in yield, due to complementation, of tenfold can be very easily detected. With this great sensitivity some degree of complementation could be shown to occur between almost any pair of allelic ts mutants, there being a continuous spectrum of yields from about 0.1 for poorly complementing pairs up to 10–50 for strongly complementing ones. In order to obtain the "non–complementary" relationships necessary to provide the overlaps which are essential for the construction of complementation maps, Bernstein et al. imposed arbitrary "cutoff" values which phage yields had to exceed before they were counted as showing complementation. The order of the mutants in the complementation map was very little affected by varying the cutoff point (Figure 5-4), and so the results do not discredit the possibility of making meaningful maps, even though they emphasize the difficulty of drawing a firm line between complementation and noncomplementation. These results are discussed further on p. 103.

It is likely that all complementation tests have built-in cutoff points due to the fact that a certain threshold level of active gene product is necessary before a positive growth response is registered. In Neurospora, as De Serres (1963) has emphasized, one gets more positive complementation tests the longer one allows for the heterokaryons to start growing. The implication of Bernstein, Denhardt, and Edgar's results is that almost any two defective forms of multimeric enzyme can form a hybrid with improved activity provided that the defects are comparatively slight, as they presumably are in temperature-sensitive and other "conditional" mutants.

5-3 DIFFERENT FORMS OF COMPLEMENTATION MAP

The simple rule for making a complementation map is that non-complementing pairs of mutants are represented as overlapping continuous lines and complementing pairs as nonoverlapping lines. A complementation map may consist of a number of segments, some coextensive with lines representing single mutants, others defined only by overlapping of such lines, and yet others defined in both ways. What gives such maps their apparent significance is the fact that a mutant can almost always be represented as a continuous line on a linear map. Even though many complementation maps have as many as ten or more segments (cf. Table 5-1), it is seldom necessary to represent a mutant by a broken line. Sometimes even though the data at first seem to show a mutant covering discontinuous regions of the map, the discontinuity can be overcome by joining the two ends of the map to form a circle (e.g., Gross, 1962; Kapuler and Bernstein, 1963). More complicated geometrical figures are sometimes necessary. For example, Costello and Bevan (1964) and Dorfman (1964) in the case of the *ad-7* locus of *Saccharomyces*, obtained a complementation map in the form of a circle with an attached linear "tail." The situation is occasionally reached in which no simple two-dimensional shape can represent the data. Leupold and Gutz (1965), working with ultraviolet-induced mutants of the *ad-6* (red) series in *Schizosaccharomyces pombe*, were able to show the complementation relationships with a map consisting of two connected circles and a small appendage (Figure 5-1). In fact, had 3 of the 18 complementation classes not been found, a simple straight line would have sufficed. When Gutz (1963) came to classify a large number of nitrous acid-induced mutants of the same series, he found one mutant which could not be represented as a continuous segment on the double-circle map, nor on any other two-dimensional map which he could devise.[2] It may be that this would be the fate of most complementation maps if larger numbers of mutants were taken into account, but it remains true that at least the great majority of the data can usually be represented by a simple geometrical figure.[3] Table 5-1 summarizes some of the features of different complementation maps.

[2] See also Costello and Bevan (1964) and Dorfman (1964).

[3] De Serres (1962) has emphasized that some apparent complexities in complementation maps in *Neurospora* may be due to unrecognized mutations,

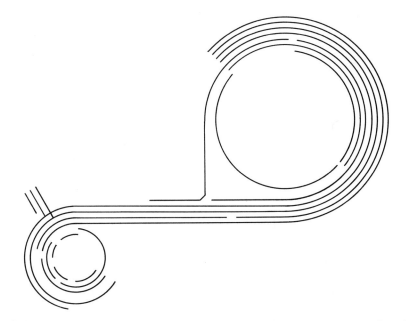

FIGURE 5-1   An example of a complex complementation map: *ad-6* of *Schizosaccharomyces pombe* (redrawn from Leupold and Gutz, 1965). The map refers only to mutants induced by ultraviolet light; if nitrous-acid-induced mutants are taken into account, even this map is too simple to represent all the data (Gutz, 1963).

Apart from differences in the shapes of the various maps, different loci differ from each other in the proportion of mutants which have to be represented as overlapping two or more segments of the map. For example, in the complementation maps of *pan-2* (Case and Giles, 1960) and *ad-4* (Woodward, Partridge, and Giles, 1958) in *Neurospora*, between a third and a half of the complementing mutants can each be represented as occupying only one segment of the map; in other words the complementation groups into which these mutants are divided are complementary in all possible combinations. At the other extreme, Gross's (1962) map of *leu-2*, also in *Neurospora*, shows only 1 complementary mutant out of 78 which occupies only a single segment; the others are all overlaps of greater or lesser length. This kind of difference may reflect real differences in the properties of the protein products of the genes concerned, or, more likely, they may merely be due to differences in the numbers

induced at the same time as the auxotrophic mutations, which interfere with heterokaryon formation.

TABLE 5-1 Summary of Some Complementation Maps

Gene	Form of map	No. of segments	No. of mutants extending over:			References
			Whole map	Two or more segments	One segment only	
Neurospora crassa						
ad-3B[*]	Straight line	2	133	0	18	De Serres (1963);
ad-3B[†]	Straight line	13	15	9	20	Brockman and De Serres (1963)
ad-4[‡]	Straight line	7	73	27	15	Woodward, Partridge, and Giles (1958)
ad-8[§]	Circle	9	(64%)	16	9	Ishikawa (1962b); Kapuler and Bernstein (1963)
am	Straight line	3	10	1	5	Fincham and Stadler (1965)
arg-1	Straight line	4	30	4	8	Catcheside and Overton (1958)
hist-1	Straight line	6	40	14	3	Catcheside (1960)
hist-2	Straight line	7	54	13	8	Catcheside (1960)
hist-3[‖]	Straight line	4	54	19	26	Catcheside (1960)
hist-5	Straight line	5	23	15	21	Catcheside (1960)
iv-2	Straight line	9	76	10	8	Bernstein and
iv-3	Straight line	4	50	33	345[#]	Miller (1961)
leu-2	Circle	18	80[**]	77	1	Gross (1962)
leu-4	Straight line	11	69	45	4	Gross and Gross (1961)
me-2	Straight line	4	32	4	8	Murray (1960)
pan-2	Straight line	6	13[††]	12	11	Case and Giles (1960)
pyr-3	Straight line	11	0	21	7	Woodward (1962)
tryp-1	Straight line	2	13	0	12	Ahmad and
tryp-3	Straight line	3	34	3	7	Catcheside (1960)

TABLE 5-1 *(continued)*

Gene	Form of map	No. of segments	No. of mutants extending over:			References
			Whole map	Two or more segments	One segment only	
Aspergillus nidulans						
"ad-9" series	Straight line	2	3	0	3	Calef and Martin-Smith, in Pontecorvo (1959)
Saccharomyces cerevisiae						
ad-2	Straight line	7	?	?	?	Bevan and Woods (1962)
ad-7	Circle + linear appendage	22	6	50	3	Costello and Bevan (1964)
	(with exceptions)	33	1	110	4	Dorfman (1964)
Schizosaccharomyces pombe						
ad-1	Straight line	4	12	21	13	Ramirez, Friis, and Leupold (1963, personal comm.)
ad-6	Two circles connected by line. No simple pattern	?	?	?	?	Ramirez, Friis, and Leupold (1963) Gutz (1963)
ad-8	Straight line	5	?	?	?	Megnet and Giles (1964)
Bacteriophage T4						
37‡‡	Straight line	9	10	11	4	Bernstein,
10‡‡	Straight line	7	0	6	4	Denhardt, and
12‡‡	Straight line	7	2	4	7	Edgar (1965)

* Spontaneous mutants.

† Mutants induced by 2-aminopurine.

‡ Mutants from all sources combined.

§ Percent noncomplementing from Ishikawa; the other numbers, from Kapuler and Bernstein, refer to the 25 distinct genetic sites—cf. Figure 5-5.

‖ Ahmed, Case, and Giles report a more complex map—cf. Figure 3-9.

Three hundred thirty-three of these were in the same complementation class and 316 arose in the same experiment—probably these were not all independent mutants.

** Maximum estimate—not all possible combinations tested.

†† Only those mutants included which are mapped genetically—probably a selected group.

‡‡ Temperature-sensitive mutants only.

of mutants available for testing. The more mutants there are, and the more complementation tests are made, the higher the proportion of overlapping mutants one would expect to find. The same argument probably applies to differences with respect to the number of segments in the complementation map. The available maps do differ widely in the numbers of segments which they show, but there is a tendency for the number to increase with the number of mutants tested. Figure 5-2 illustrates this point. While there is no reason to doubt that real differences do exist between genes in the maximum number of complementation segments obtainable there is little indication that this maximum has been approached in any case investigated up to the present. The total number of potentially identifiable segments seems in general to be large.

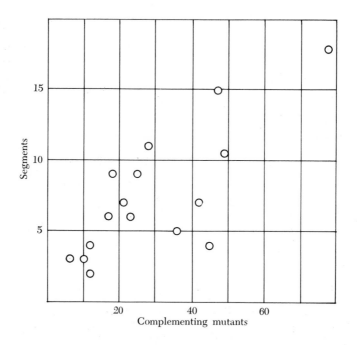

FIGURE 5-2   The data of Table 5-1 plotted to show the tendency for the complexity of complementation maps, as reflected in the number of segments in the map, to increase as more complementing mutants are found. Only the *Neurospora* data are included.

5-4 THE MEANING OF COMPLEMENTATION MAPS

What are they maps of? The first few complementation maps which were made encouraged two generalizations. The first was that complementation maps were always linear and two-ended, and the second was that the order of the segments in the complementation map was the same as the order of the corresponding mutational sites in the genetic map. If these two generalizations were true it would be reasonable to regard complementation maps as maps of the genes themselves or of molecules of template ("messenger") RNA transcribed directly from the genes. This in turn would suggest that recombination could occur between homologous template RNA molecules much as between homologous chromosomes. Such an idea was, in fact, seriously considered at the time of the earlier work on interallelic complementation in *Neurospora* (Woodward, Partridge, and Giles, 1958; Fincham, 1958).

As we saw in the last chapter, the whole trend of recent research is against the suggestion that complementation can occur at the RNA level and supports instead the hybrid protein hypothesis, according to which interallelic complementation occurs through co-aggregation, probably with conformational correction, of polypeptide chains. It seems, then, that complementation maps must be maps of polypeptide subunits of proteins. Such subunits could conceivably be fully extended chains, but are much more likely to be folded in various specific and complex ways. On this view, a complementation map only represents the gene at third hand, and as a picture of gene structure it is likely to be considered distorted by the folding of the polypeptide chain to form the three-dimensional protein subunit.

Do complementation maps have any structural meaning? What is the meaning of the order of the segments in a complementation map? First, one must take account of the possibility that it may have no straightforward connection with the geometrical structure of the protein. The point may be illustrated by reference to the speculations made in the last chapter on the mechanism of complementation between mutant varieties of glutamate dehydrogenase in *Neurospora*. It was suggested that one complementing mutant (am^1) produces a protein which had a normal conformation and which could correct the conformation of other kinds of mutant protein in a hybrid multimer but which had lost some essential group of the catalytically active center. Some other mutants (am^2, am^3,

am^{19}), complementary to am^1, produce proteins which are enzymically active when in the correct conformation, which they usually are not. Another kind of mutant (am^{14}), complementary to all the others mentioned, may possibly produce a mutant polypeptide which cannot form multimers by itself but can do so, and provide both an active center and a near-normal conformation, when hybridized with mutant subunits of other kinds. On this interpretation the three segments in the *am* complementation map may represent three different qualities of the protein: the possession of the active center, ability to impose a normal conformation, and ability to aggregate. These qualities, with the exception of the active center, are very likely not attributes of particular segments of the polypeptide chain but rather of the structure as a whole. The overlaps which give a linear order to the map may mean no more than that certain combinations of qualities, for example, aggregatability and normal conformation, or normal conformation and a component of the active center, are apt to be lost together as a result of certain mutations. With so few complementing mutants the apparent linearity of the map may be no more than fortuitous. Figure 5-3 summarizes the present information on complementation between *am* mutants of *Neurospora*.

The principle of homologous correction. Where the number of segments becomes larger, and the consistency of a simple (often

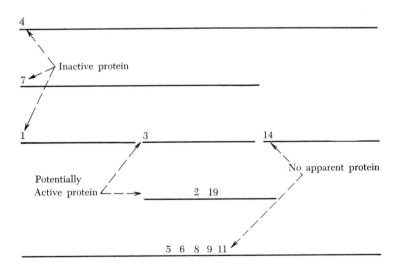

FIGURE 5-3   Complementation map of the *am* (glutamate dehydrogenase) locus of *Neurospora* compared with what is known of the products of the mutant alleles. From data of Fincham and Stadler (1965).

linear) arrangement of these segments becomes more impressive, it begins to seem almost certain that complementation maps do really mean something in terms of protein structure. How may one attempt to decipher this meaning?

Let us assume that, in general, complementing mutants produce protein subunits with conformational abnormalities which are capable of correction. There may well be complementing mutants which do not come into this category (perhaps the mutant am^1 of *Neurospora*, discussed on p. 85, is a case in point), but our assumption seems likely to be true more often than not. We need not specify the nature of the conformational defects, and they may be of various different kinds, but they might often take the form of unraveling of a-helical secondary structure.

In order for two conformationally defective mutant subunits to complement each other, at least one must be able to correct the other's defect; in most cases, one would guess, the correction would have to be mutual. It is evident that each subunit is unable to correct *itself* in an aggregate, otherwise it would not be defective and would not be recognized as mutant. Therefore the region which has to be corrected in each subunit must be partly or wholly *homologous with* the region whose *normal* structure is needed for its correction.[4] The correcting region can thus only be supplied by a normal subunit, or a mutant subunit with a defect which does *not* overlap (i.e., which is entirely nonhomologous with) that of the subunit to be corrected. It is evident that this concept of overlapping or nonoverlapping defective regions of complementing mutant protein subunits is formally equivalent to the overlapping or nonoverlapping lines on a complementation map.

It thus seems reasonable, as a working hypothesis, to equate segments on the complementation map with definite regions of the corresponding protein subunit in which homologous correction can occur. This hypothesis represents a somewhat simplified view of the situation and may well be oversimple in some instances. This is because the region of the complementation map occupied by a mutant is not a function of that mutant alone, but also depends on the nature of the other mutants against which it is tested for complementation. It is unrealistic to suppose that there will usually be a sharp dividing line between conformationally distorted and normal parts of a mutant protein. One can easily imagine that a region on the fringe of a conformational distortion may act as

[4] The mutual correction of two *deformed* regions is a possibility, but does not seem a reasonable *general* explanation of complementation maps (see Crick and Orgel, 1964).

essentially "normal" (in the sense of being able to form part of a correcting region) in some interallelic combinations but not in others. The relative nature of complementation segments, and evidence that they do nevertheless have some objective meaning, is discussed further in a subsequent section.

Whether the shape of a complementation map can be taken literally as indicating the shape of the protein subunit depends on how conformational distortions spread through the molecule from the point of the primary mutational disturbances. It is, of course, the way that the defects in different mutant subunits spread and overlap that must define the shape of the map. If the conformational distortion were always transmitted along the polypeptide chain, then the order of the segments in the complementation map would be the same as the order of the corresponding regions in the extended polypeptide. This may often be approximately true, but one would also expect that sometimes, because of folding, the spreading of a distortion might occur between regions which are relatively far apart in the amino acid sequence but which are close together in the folded structure.

This possibility is well illustrated by Gross's (1962) interpretation of the mechanism of complementation at the *leu-2* locus of *Neurospora*. He made the striking observation that the efficiency of complementation of over half of the normally complementary pairs of *leu-2* mutants was drastically reduced by the presence of a *leu-3* mutation in one of the nuclei of the heterokaryon. So far as the biochemical data go they indicate that *leu-2* and *leu-3* mutants are defective in the same enzyme (catalyzing the interconversion of the α- and β-isomers of hydroxy-β-carboxyisocaproate), and the suggestion is that the two genes, which are not linked, determine the structure of two different polypeptide components of this enzyme. If this is correct, it seems that a defect in one kind of chain in the aggregate can upset the mutual correction of two chains of a different kind. If an interaction of this type can occur between nonhomologous chains it may also be expected between different parts of the sequences of homologous chains. Thus noncomplementation does not necessarily mean that the mutants in question have defects in the same part of the amino acid sequence of the polypeptide chain, though it may still be taken as indicating that they are defective in the same region of the *folded structure*.

No matter how conformational distortions are transmitted through the protein, so long as such transmission occurs in a continuous way, without "jumping" of regions, complementation maps must provide some kind of picture of the spatial arrangement of the independently distortable and correctible regions of the protein subunit.

Graded spreading effects reflected in complementation maps. That mutational distortions do often spread through protein structure in a reasonably orderly way is indicated by the data of Bernstein, Denhardt, and Edgar (1965) on complementation of *ts* mutants of bacteriophage T4. As was explained earlier, the great majority of intragenic combinations of *ts* mutants show some degree of complementation, so if one represents even slightly complementing mutants by nonoverlapping complementation segments one has hardly any overlaps with which to determine the order of the segments. To make the mapping possible it is necessary to establish an arbitrary level of complementation (cutoff point) below which mutants are shown as overlapping. The significant observation was that almost the same order of segments was arrived at no matter what cutoff point was fixed upon. Figure 5-4 illustrates this for one gene. The implication is that as one moves away from the center of the region of disruption caused by a given mutation, the severity of the distortion gradually decreases. Thus two mutant protein subunits with their centers of mutational disruption overlapping would hardly complement at all, whereas if only the fringes of the affected regions overlapped they might complement quite well.

Kapuler and Bernstein's model. It should be particularly instructive to compare the complementation map of a gene with the genetic map showing the order of the mutational sites in the DNA. Following the definitive studies of Yanofsky *et al.* (1964) on *Escherichia coli* and of Sarabhai *et al.* (1964) on T4 bacteriophage we can assume with a fair degree of assurance that the positions of the mutant sites in an accurate map of a gene represent the positions of the corresponding amino acid substitutions in the polypeptide chain which is the gene product. The spacing of the sites may not be precisely the same as the spacing of the corresponding amino acids in the polypeptide chain (since the frequency of genetic exchange may not be uniform throughout the gene), but at any rate the two orders should correspond. In fact, Yanofsky's data indicate that, in his example at least, the genetic map gives a surprisingly accurate picture of the polypeptide chain as regards both order *and* spacing. Thus, given a gene map one can ask what kind of folding of the corresponding polypeptide chain might explain the observed complementation map.

The picture of protein structure which one reads into complementation maps depends on how one thinks homologous correction

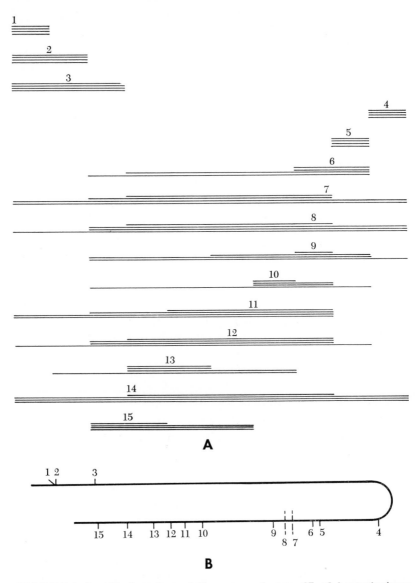

FIGURE 5-4   (A) Complementation map of gene 37 of bacteriophage T4, based on mixed infection of *E. coli* cells with temperature-sensitive mutants. The four bars for each mutant represent complementation assessed by reference to four different cutoff points: respectively 0.25, 0.75, 2.5, and 7.5% of wild-type yield of phage particles per cell at 40°C, taking the bars in order from the upper to the lower. Note that as the cutoff is raised, the changing comple-

occurs. The obvious assumption to make is that there must be a close juxtaposition of homologous regions of subunits in the multimeric protein molecule. The complexity of many complementation maps, with their numerous segments, often representing many classes of mutants complementary in all combinations, would seem to require that such close juxtaposition occurred *at many points.*

How could such an extensive point-for-point association of subunits be achieved? There would be no problem here if one were able to assume that extended polypeptide chains paired like homologous chromosomes *prior to* folding, producing something like a folded multistranded cable. Nothing that we know about the ways in which polypeptide chains are arranged in multimeric proteins (which is admittedly rather little) encourages such a model. It seems much more likely that most proteins are better pictured as aggregates of already folded subunits rather than as formed by folding superimposed upon a homologous alignment of extended polypeptide chains. This leads to a difficulty. A number of identical or quasi-identical three-dimensional folded structures might form an aggregate, but it is not immediately obvious how they could be arranged so that a whole series of homologous segments of different subunits could be closely associated. Two kinds of solution to this problem have been suggested.

The first possibility, suggested by Kapuler and Bernstein (1963) in their analysis of complementation at *ad-8* in *Neurospora,* is that the folded subunits are essentially two-dimensional and form a stack, all with the same side uppermost and with corresponding regions superimposed. In this way every part of each subunit would be close to the homologous regions of neighboring subunits. The relationship between neighboring subunits would not be a symmetrical

mentation relationships can be represented simply by extension of segments. In many cases one has a choice as to which segments should be extended; in this figure, mutants 1–4 are arbitrarily represented by the same segments throughout. In order to make the representation consistent, two phage yields were assumed to be slightly on the "wrong" side of a cutoff through sampling error. Based on data of Bernstein, Denhardt, and Edgar (1965).

(B) Suggested conformation of the polypeptide product of gene 37, to explain the relation between the genetic and complementation maps. After Bernstein, Denhardt, and Edgar (1965).

one, however, since the "upper" surface of one would be in contact with the "lower" surface of the next (Figure 5-6).

An attractive feature of Kapuler and Bernstein's model is that it permits one to deduce the form of the hypothetical protein subunit from that of the complementation map. Thus a two-ended linear map would suggest a flattened rod, a closed loop an annular shape, and more complex maps correspondingly more involved structures. Kapuler and Bernstein went further. They assumed that the site of the primary amino acid substitution brought about by a mutation always falls within the region of disruption which is represented by the corresponding segment on the complementation map. Actually, as explained below, this assumption may well be wrong in many cases, but we may accept it as likely to be true more often than not. On this basis, and regarding the genetic map of *ad-8* as a reliable representation of the sequence of mutant sites in the polypeptide chain, Kapuler and Bernstein derived a model for the conformation of the chain in the folded protein subunit. They found that by winding the gene map about one and a half times round the circular complementation map [5] they were able to bring the mutational sites in the former into alignment with the corresponding segments in the latter. Figure 5-5 illustrates how this fit was achieved, and Figure 5-6 the interpretation in terms of protein structure.

Later Bernstein, in collaboration with Denhardt and Edgar (1965) applied the same principle to three genes in bacteriophage T4, using the complementation maps based on temperature-sensitive mutants. The results for one gene, and the conclusions drawn about the possible conformation of the protein subunits, were shown in Figure 5-4.

If Bernstein's procedure is valid it provides a powerful tool for investigating the conformations of proteins without doing any physics or chemistry—"the poor man's Fourier analysis," to use an optimistic phrase (Edgar, personal communication). There are, however, reasons for regarding it as oversimple. An assumption which may not always be justified is that the distorted region of the mutant subunit which can be corrected by a normal homologous region always includes the amino acid substitution which is, presumably, the primary effect of the mutation. While this seems likely to be the general rule, it cannot be excluded that some amino acid substitutions may have their most critical effects on the folding of sections of the chain in which they themselves are not included. Furthermore, the nonsymmetrical relationship between subunits,

---

[5] Ishikawa (1965) now believes that the complementation map should be a straight line, not a circle (cf. legend to Figure 3-4).

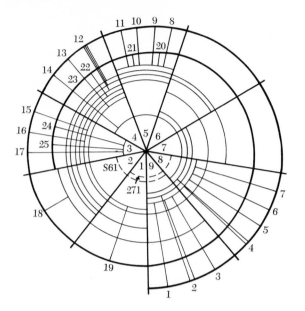

FIGURE 5-5 Kapuler and Bernstein's (1963) correlation of the genetic and complementation maps of the *ad-8* (adenylosuccinate synthetase) locus of *Neurospora crassa,* based on data of Ishikawa (1962b). The circular complementation map, with its nine segments shown arbitrarily as equal sectors, is on the inside. The genetic map, with 25 sites of complementing mutants numbered in order, is wound one and a half times round the complementation map in such a way as to permit the genetic sites to be joined to corresponding complementation segments by radial lines. Two mutants, S61 (site 23) and 271 (site 16) do not fit this representation. When two or more patterns of complementation occur among mutants at the same site two or more radial lines are drawn (i.e., sites 2, 4, and 12). Reproduced from Kapuler and Bernstein (1963).

which is a feature of Bernstein's type of model, does not look realistic to crystallographers, who are accustomed to the subunits of aggregates being related by axes of symmetry.

Complementation with protein subunits related by an axis of symmetry. There are very few examples of multimeric proteins in which the three-dimensional arrangement of the subunits is known. In hemoglobin, as is well known, there is a twofold axis of symmetry —that is to say, an axis about which the molecule can be rotated so that its initial aspect recurs identically after 180 deg as well as after 360 deg of rotation. Some information of the arrangement of

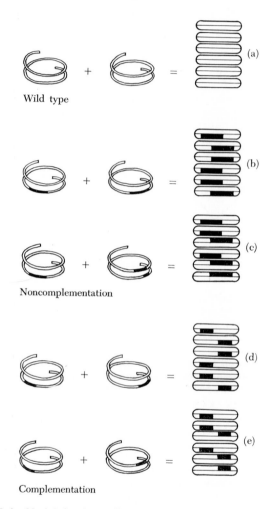

Wild type

Noncomplementation

Complementation

FIGURE 5-6   Model for interallelic complementation at the *Neurospora*
ad-8 locus (cf. Figure 5-4). The subunit of the enzyme
(adenylosuccinate synthetase) is pictured as a near-
planar spiral, and the whole enzyme as a layered stack
of such units. Defects in subunit structures resulting from
mutation are represented as black segments. Normal segments can correct homologous defective ones; where
defects overlap, complementation is not possible. From
Kapuler and Bernstein (1963).

subunits in larger protein multimers is available from electron microscopy. The protein shells (capsids) of simple viruses, which are usually multimers of a high order, always seem to have manyfold axes of symmetry (Markham *et al.*, 1963). Most enzymic proteins are too small to be amenable to electron microscopic analysis, but Horne and Greville (1963) have produced pictures of ox liver glutamate dehydrogenase which show fairly convincingly a threefold symmetry, and may be interpreted as suggesting that the 250,000-molecular-weight subunit (cf. Table 4-1, p. 66) is composed of monomers forming the six sides of a tetrahedron. Thus there are some grounds for suggesting that symmetry is a general feature of multimeric proteins.

Crick and Orgel (1964) have discussed reasonable models for complementation between subunits related by an axis of symmetry. There is, however, one limitation which arises from such a relationship. This is that homologous regions of different subunits will only come close together in the vicinity of the axis of rotation. The simplest example is a dimer with a twofold (dyad) symmetry axis. Even if the subunits are fairly flat with a large surface of near-contact, their symmetry will require that the "left-hand" half of one will be opposed to the "right-hand" half of the other, and vice versa. Only near the dyad axis will homologous regions be juxtaposed, and even here each stretch of polypeptide chain, unless it runs parallel to the axis, will be in reversed sequence relative to its homologue. Figure 5-7 shows an imaginary dimer in which homologous regions of the two subunits come close together at several points along the dyad axis. Such discontinuous axial regions would probably be represented on the complementation map as distinct segments. Mutants overlapping two or more such regions could be due to spreading effects of one kind or another, the transmission of the effects occurring either along the polypeptide chain or by interactions between segments down the dyad axis. In most mutants conformational disruption would presumably be centered around the site of the primary amino acid substitution though, as was pointed out in the discussion of the Kapuler-Bernstein model, this may not be true in all cases.

Why linearity? Since interactions between different parts of a folded polypeptide chain are likely to be many and varied, one would expect simple linear complementation maps to be, at most, the general trend rather than the invariable rule. From this point of view it is no surprise that more complex maps are sometimes necessary. Again, it is not unexpected that such correlation as does exist between complementation and genetic maps should be far from per-

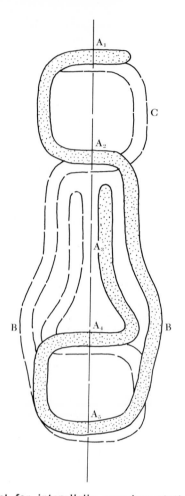

FIGURE 5-7   Model for interallelic complementation where the gene
product is a dimer, with normally identical folded polypeptide chains related by a twofold symmetry axis
(broken line). The subunits would probably have some
secondary (probably α-helical) folding structure under-
lying the tertiary folding shown here. A_1, A_2, etc., are
regions near the symmetry axis where homologous segments of the two subunits are juxtaposed. In each of
these regions it is supposed that a normal segment can
correct a homologous conformationally defective one.
A region such as A_3 running parallel to the dyad axis,
with relatively extensive homologous pairing, might contain several independently distortable and correctible
regions and thus correspond to several complementation
segments. It is possible that conformational correction

fect. Genetically close mutants will necessarily have their amino acid substitutions, and hence, probably, their regions of disruption, close together in the protein, whereas genetically distant ones (still within one gene) are *likely* to affect well-separated parts of the folded chain, but whenever the polypeptide chain turns and doubles back along a dyad axis one would expect discrepancies between the two kinds of map. As we have seen, such discrepancies were interpreted by Kapuler and Bernstein (1963) in a rather direct way as indicating patterns of folding of the polypeptide chain. On an axis-of-symmetry type of model they would provide, at best, a picture of those parts of the subunit structure close to the dyad axis.

Complementation involving highly multimeric proteins. The preceding argument has been developed particularly with reference to dimers with twofold symmetry. Essentially the same principle, that homologous regions of subunits will be associated in parts of the structure close to the axis of symmetry, applies to multimers with manyfold symmetry. It is perhaps more difficult to imagine a large number of regions of *close* homologous association within a high multimer, simply because the subunits (unless they are two-dimensional structures running parallel to the axis of symmetry) will tend to get in each other's way as they are moved closer to the axis. Nevertheless multimeric proteins are common, and almost all complementation maps, at least when based on numerous mutants, have many segments (cf. Table 5-1). The answer to this difficulty, if it is a difficulty, may be that many higher multimers are built up from dimers, each one with its own dyad axis.

If one accepts a model of the kind proposed by Kapuler and Bernstein, high multimers present no special problem. Any number of subunits can be stacked, each one having the same relationship to the units below and above.

---

could also occur between nonhomologous segments, as at B, but this would permit mutual correction of two *identical* mutant chains (i.e., the mutant could correct itself). A mutation having its main effect in a region away from the axis such as C might sometimes interfere with homologous correction in two adjacent regions (A_1 and A_2), thus causing an overlap on the complementation map. Note that in this particular version of the model the order of the homologously paired regions down the dyad axis is *not* the same as the order of the corresponding segments in the extended polypeptide chain. Based on Crick and Orgel (1964 and personal communication).

5-5 CONCLUSIONS

The making of complementation maps can be interesting and is often a useful way of condensing many data into a compact diagram, but perhaps it is sometimes given too much importance in the present state of our knowledge. The homologous correction principle seems likely to be valid, and Crick and Orgel's explanation of how it works is very attractive, but it is difficult to see how to prove their very general and flexible concept without actually determining, for example by crystallographic methods, the actual three-dimensional structures of mutant, wild-type, and complementation enzyme varieties in some particular cases. This is so formidable a program that one may doubt whether it will be carried out for many decades. Nevertheless it may still be worthwhile comparing the forms of complementation maps with the general nature of the corresponding proteins. Particularly relevant would be information on the number of monomers in the multimer, the general overall shape of the monomers and the multimer, and the kind of symmetry, if any, prevailing in the multimer. Where there is no possibility of gaining information on the structure of the protein, it is probably not worthwhile to put much effort into the construction of an elaborate complementation map, since its physical meaning will always be in doubt.

6

THE POSSIBLE EVOLUTIONARY
SIGNIFICANCE OF ALLELIC
COMPLEMENTATION

So far we have considered complementation only in relation to grossly defective mutant alleles. Is interallelic complementation merely an interesting and instructive artifact, or is it also a factor in the genetics of natural populations?

6-1 THEORIES OF HETEROSIS

The firm establishment of the possibility of truly complementary action of alleles supplies a possible solution to a long-standing problem in population genetics. The phenomenon of *heterosis,* that is of the tendency for hybrid diploid individuals to exceed their pure-bred parents in size and vigor, has long been known in higher plants and animals. Though hybrid vigor has been put to great practical use, particularly in the development of high-yielding varieties of hybrid maize, there has always been uncertainty about how it should be explained. Two rival, though not necessarily incompatible, theories have been put forward.

The first theory, long advocated by D. F. Jones (1917; and see,

113

for example, his article in Gowen, 1952) explains heterosis as due to *intergenic* complementation. The argument runs that any species which is normally outbred is likely to carry a large number of recessive genes which are deleterious when homozygous. If these deleterious recessives are present individually in low frequency, homozygosity for any one of them, requiring the mating of two individuals both carrying the gene in question, will be rare. Thus so long as the population remains crossbred these deleterious recessives will have little obvious effect. However, self-fertilization or close inbreeding will at once produce homozygosis for one or more deleterious recessives in many, perhaps nearly all, of the progeny, leading to the decline in vigor which is empirically observed when normally outbreeding species are inbred. In different inbred lines different recessives will become "fixed," depending on which ones happened to be present in the individuals used to found each line. Thus one line might be *aa BB CC* in constitution, a second *AA bb CC*, and a third *AA BB cc*, where *a, b,* and *c* are deleterious recessive genes and *A, B,* and *C* their dominant alleles. Crossing any two of these will give a first generation (F₁) hybrid in which each deleterious recessive is "covered" by its dominant allele, with restoration of the vigor characteristic of the original outbred population.

The implication of this theory is that it is possible, in principle, to bring all the desirable dominant genes into the same individual in homozygous condition (i.e., *AA BB CC*) and thus obtain something equivalent to heterotic vigor in a pure line. There should be no advantage in heterozygosity as such. Repeated attempts to "fix" heterotic vigor, especially in maize, where it is of great commercial importance, have however failed. This failure can be explained away by saying that the number of deleterious recessives "floating" in the original population, and hence the number of desirable dominants which one would have to get homozygous, is so large that the chance of avoiding getting at least one deleterious recessive fixed in any inbred line is negligible. This could be so, especially if, as first suggested by Jones (1917), many of the desirable dominants are linked to deleterious recessives. Yet one might still hope to be able to recover, from each heterotic hybrid, *relatively* good inbred lines with at least some of the undesirable genes bred out. Pairs of these, selected for the vigor of their hybrids, could then be used for a further cycle of selection, and so on, until virtually all the deleterious recessives had been got rid of. Though programs of this kind have seemed successful at first, there seems to be a limit to the progress which can be made along these lines (Hull, 1952). The suspicion has grown that complementary action of genes at different loci is not the whole explanation of heterosis.

The second theory, advanced by East (1936), involves *interallelic* complementation. It supposes that, for certain genes, heterozygosity may be advantageous *in itself*. Thus two alleles A^1 and A^2 might exist such that the heterozygote A^1/A^2 was larger or more vigorous than either A^1/A^1 *or* A^2/A^2, other genes being the same. This phenomenon, which for a long time was rather hypothetical, was called *overdominance*, since the phenotype was supposed to surpass what would have been obtained had the more effective of the two alleles been completely dominant over the other. Overdominance is essentially synonymous with interallelic complementation. The main reason for disbelieving the overdominance theory was the difficulty of seeing how it could work at the level of gene action. As we saw in Chapter 2, the widely accepted view of the gene as a unit of function was hard to reconcile with complementary action of alleles. The recent demonstrations in microorganisms of the near-universality of interallelic complementation has completely altered the picture. There is now no theoretical obstacle to believing in the *possibility* of overdominance as a frequent and significant factor in the genetics and evolution of populations.

The reasons for believing that interallelic complementation is of significance in nature can be considered under three heads. First, there are numerous examples of "hybrid" protein products of the interaction of naturally occurring alleles. Second, one can argue, although without very much real evidence at the present time, that these hybrid products are often functionally superior to the homomultimers produced by homozygotes. Finally, some regularly heteromultimeric proteins have distinct polypeptide chains which, although now under the control of different genes, have enough amino acid sequence in common to suggest that originally they were controlled by alleles of the same gene. Such cases suggest that interallelic complementation may be a stage in the evolution of heteromultimeric proteins.

6-2 THE OCCURRENCE OF INTERALLELIC HYBRID PROTEINS

Hybrid antigens. The first evidence for "hybrid" products of allelic interaction came from studies of antigens in birds. Irwin and Cole (reviewed by Irwin, 1951) and Irwin and Cumley (1945) in-

TABLE 6-1 Tests Distinguishing between Different Ring Dove–Pearlneck "Hybrid" Substances Associated with Various Unit Antigens Specific to Pearlneck †

Cells	Anti-F_1 absorbed by cells of both species		Anti-F_1 ($172F_1$) ‡ absorbed by cells of both species *and* cells of F_1 or backcross hybrids containing the antigens listed									
	Most sera	$172F_1$	d-1	d-2	d-3	d-4	d-7	d-9	d-10	d-11	d-12	F_1
Pearlneck	0	0	0	0	0	0	0	0	0	0	0	0
Ring dove	0	0	0	0	0	0	0	0	0	0	0	0
F_1 hybrid	++	+++	++	++	++	++	++	++	++	+	++	0
Backcross progeny:												
d-1	0	++	0	0	0	±	0	0	0	+	0	0
d-2	0	++	0	0	0	+	0	0	0	+	0	0
d-3	0	++	0	0	0	0	0	0	0	+	0	0
d-4	+	±*				0						
d-5	0	0										
d-6	0	0										
d-7	0	+	0	0	0	+	0	0	0	+	0	0
d-9	0	++	0	0	0	0	0	0	0	±	0	0
d-10	0	++	0	0	0	+	0	0	0	+	0	0
d-11	+	++	+	+	+	+	+	+	+	0	+	0
d-12		+	0	0	0	0	0	0	0	±	0	0

† Slightly abridged from Irwin and Cumley (1945).
‡ $172F_1$ was an unusually potent serum used for identifying dx-B—see text; * indicates unexpected weak reaction attributed to old serum with decayed anti-dx-C antibodies.

vestigated the red blood cell antigens distinguishing species of the dove family (Columbidae). The species pair *Streptopelia chinensis* (pearlneck) and *Streptopelia risoria* (ring dove) were particularly studied. An immune serum prepared against blood cells of one bird and then exhaustively absorbed with cells from another would only agglutinate cells carrying antigens present in the first bird and absent in the second. By absorbing antisera, prepared against parental or F_1 hybrid cells, with cells of different individuals from the ring dove $\times$ F_1 backcross, a series of reagents were prepared for a series of unit antigens present in pearlneck but not in ring dove. In general the inheritance of these antigens was very clear cut. The F_1 birds produced all the antigens of both parents, while the ring dove $\times F_1$ backcross progenies showed clear one-to-one segregation of presence versus absence of each antigen differentiating pearlneck from ring dove. This was some of the earliest evidence implicating specific genes in the determination of the structures of specific macromolecules.

The only disturbing feature was the fact that antiserum prepared against cells of the F_1 hybrid could *not* be exhausted of antibodies by treatment with the cells of the two parents. After this treatment there still remained some antibodies which agglutinated F_1 cells but neither kind of parent cell. This showed that one or more antigens were peculiar to the hybrid, occurring in neither parent. Further investigation showed that the "hybrid substances" could be analyzed into two or three fractions. One (dx-A) was produced by the interaction of a pearlneck gene, which was closely linked to or identical with the determinant of the pearlneck d-11 antigen, with something in the ring dove genome. A second (dx-C), for which the evidence was somewhat less satisfactory (cf. Table 6-1), was apparently due to an interaction involving a gene closely linked to or identical with the determinant of the pearlneck d-4 antigen. The third (dx-B), which usually accounted only for a small part of the hybrid antigenic activity, was identified in a number of the backcross progeny carrying a number of different pearlneck antigen-determining genes (d-1, d-2, d-3, d-7, d-9, d-10, d-12). The pearlneck factor(s) involved in the formation of dx-B was, however, shown to be separable from these other genes in further backcrosses to ring dove. Irwin and Cumley suggested that the formation of dx-B might be the result of the interaction of any one of a number of pearlneck genes, with duplicate effects, with the ring dove genome, but it is not clear that the same pearlneck gene was not involved in each case. Some data are summarized in Table 6-1.

A rather similar result was obtained by Bryan and Miller (1953) with hybrids of the common pigeon (*Columba livia*) and an African species (*C. guinea*). They were able to obtain a serological reagent to an antigen present in the red blood cells of all birds heterozygous for a pair of allelic antigens differentiating the two species but absent from the cells of all birds of either homozygous type. Hybrid antigens have also been reported in species hybrids in ducks (Mc-Gibbon, 1944).

More recently, Finger and Heller (1963) have obtained evidence for a rather different kind of hybrid antigen in variety 2 of the ciliate *Paramecium aurelia*. They studied a range of genotypes producing serologically distinguishable surface antigens of the C series, and the F_1 hybrids between them. They found that the F_1 animals usually possessed the antigenic determinants of *both* parents; no search was made for unique hybrid antigens not present in either parent. However, whereas a mixture of isolated C antigens from two different homozygous types could be resolved into its two components by diffusion in agar gels, the F_1 hybrid appeared, in most cases, to have both antigenic determinants associated with a single type of molecule, since they could not be separated. Thus a heterozygote seemed to be able to form a hybrid antigenic molecule not, as in the examples from birds quoted above, necessarily with any new specificity, but with a *combination* of parental specificities.

All these examples of hybrid antigens can very reasonably be explained as due to the formation of hybrid proteins by interaction of allelic polypeptide chains, as discussed in the previous two chapters. Where the hybridization results in some mutual modification of conformation a new antigenic specificity might well result.

Hybrid enzymes. The development of techniques for zone electrophoresis of proteins in starch or polyacrylamide gels, and for staining specifically for various enzyme activities in such gels, has given greatly increased opportunities for detecting the existence of different varieties of particular enzymes within species and of hybrid enzymes in heterozygotes. Phosphatases, peptidases, esterases, and pyridine nucleotide-linked dehydrogenases can be revealed as sharp colored bands in gels by specific staining procedures. The hydrolyzing enzymes can be made to yield highly colored insoluble products through the use of appropriate chromogenic substrates, while the dehydrogenases can be made to reduce tetrazolium salts to red or purple formazan dyes by using some artificial electron carrier, such as phenazine methosulfate, to couple oxidation of pyridine nucleotide to the reduction of the tetrazolium derivative.

Schwartz's (1960, 1962, 1964) studies on the esterases of maize were among the first to give clear evidence of hybrid enzyme formation through allelic interaction. He has identified two esterases in maize extracts active at pH 7.5. They are controlled by two different genes. Electrophoretically distinct variants of each enzyme exist in different maize stocks, and each variant is controlled by an allele of the gene controlling the enzyme in question. Three alleles of one gene have been identified and two of the other. In any plant heterozygous with respect to two alleles determining electrophoretically distinct esterase varieties, a "hybrid" enzyme in an electrophoretically intermediate position was detected in addition to the two parental-type enzymes.

Other examples of hybrid enzymes formed by allelic interactions were found in the fruit fly *Drosophila melanogaster* by Johnson and his colleagues. Beckman and Johnson (1964) found that different stocks of flies had electrophoretically different forms of alkaline phosphatase. F_1 hybrids produced, in addition to both parental enzyme varieties, an electrophoretically intermediate phosphatase not present in either parent. Genetic studies indicated that the two parental phosphatase varieties were controlled by two alleles of a single gene, and that individuals carrying both alleles always produced both varieties plus the "hybrid" phosphatase. Johnson and Denniston (1964) found a very similar situation with respect to alcohol dehydrogenase in *Drosophila*. The Canton S strain, unlike the others tested, produced a variety of the enzyme with an unusually low electrophoretic mobility. F_1 flies obtained by crossing strains with "fast" and "slow" alcohol dehydrogenases produced both varieties, with, in addition, an electrophoretically intermediate enzyme band. Here again the two parental enzyme varieties seemed to be controlled by two alleles, and heterozygosity for these two alleles was always associated with the formation of the hybrid enzyme (see Figure 6-1). A precisely analogous situation, involving two electrophoretically distinct acid phosphatases, was described by Allen, Misch, and Morrison (1963) in the ciliate *Tetrahymena*.

While there is no proof in any of these cases that the electrophoretically intermediate component is a hybrid,[1] this seems overwhelmingly probable. The general impression is that wherever electrophoretically distinct, allelically controlled proteins are produced in the same cell a hybrid is likely also to occur.

In fact, perhaps more interest attaches to cases where a hybrid is

---

[1] But see Scandalios's (1965) very beautiful demonstration of multiple hybrid catalase varieties in *Zea mays*.

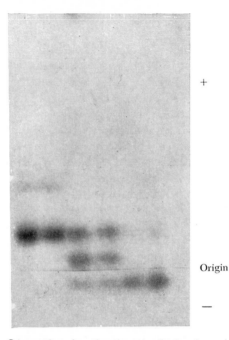

+

Origin

—

FIGURE 6-1   Separation by starch gel electrophoresis at pH 8.65 of different forms of alcohol dehydrogenase (ADH) formed by various strains of *Drosophila melanogaster*. The positions of the ADH bands are revealed by a specific staining mixture. In the first and second lanes (reading from the left) are samples of extracts of flies true-breeding for a fast-running negatively charged ADH variety. In the fifth and sixth lanes are extracts of flies true-breeding for a slow-running positively charged ADH variety. The third and fourth lanes contain extracts of F_1 hybrids between the two true-breeding strains. Note the formation of an intermediate ("hybrid") enzyme variety in the F_1 flies. There is also a fainter and more negatively charged band corresponding to each of the major bands; this may be an indication that each enzyme variety, including the hybrid, exists in two electrophoretically distinct forms. From Johnson and Denniston (1964).

not found. Johnson and Sakai (1964) observed three electrophoretic forms of leucine aminopeptidase in *Drosophila buskii,* but no evident hybrid enzymes were present in heterozygotes. Also in *Drosophila,* Young, Porter, and Childs (1964) demonstrated two electrophoretic forms of glucose-6-phosphate dehydrogenase controlled by two alleles of a sex-linked gene. The two enzyme varieties were beautifully resolved by electrophoresis of heterozygote extracts and there was clearly no intermediate enzyme band. In *Neurospora*, Horowitz *et al.* (1961) have never observed any electrophoretically intermediate tyrosinase in heterokaryons carrying nuclei determining different electrophoretic forms of the enzyme. In cases such as these the absence of any apparent hybrid protein may simply mean that the enzyme in question is monomeric. It is also possible, however, that the electrophoretic difference observed between the homozygous (or homokaryotic) strains was not due to a difference with respect to the content of acidic or basic amino acid side chains but rather to a difference in conformation. The hybrid, even if formed, might in this case resemble one "parent" protein rather than the other in conformation and thus not be distinguished as an intermediate band. This possibility is raised by the observations of Sundaram and Fincham (1964) on an electrophoretically different glutamate dehydrogenase in *Neurospora*, which was discussed in Chapter 4.

For a number of years the clearest case of failure of hybrid formation when different homologous polypeptide chains of a multimeric protein were being produced in the same cell appeared to be human hemoglobin. Numerous electrophoretically distinct varieties of both the alpha and beta chains of hemoglobin are known (Baglioni, 1963), and blood of individuals heterozygous with respect to alpha or beta chain varieties has often been analyzed by electrophoresis. Although alpha-beta hybrid hemoglobins (i.e., a_1a_1 $\beta_2\beta_2$ or a_2a_2 $\beta_1\beta_1$) are easily observed in individuals heterozygous with respect to both kinds of chain, alpha-alpha hybrids (i.e., a_1a_2 $\beta\beta$) or beta-beta hybrids (i.e., aa $\beta_1\beta_2$) are not usually observable. It has recently been suggested, however, that the explanation may be not that the latter kinds of hybrid cannot be formed, but that they are in rapidly established equilibrium with the nonhybrid species of molecule under the fractionation conditions, and so tend to dehybridize with formation of the "pure" types as the fractionation proceeds (Guidotti, Konigsberg, and Craig, 1963).

6-3 POSSIBLE FUNCTIONAL SIGNIFICANCE AND EVOLUTIONARY STABILIZATION OF HETEROMULTIMERS

There is no indication in any of the examples of hybrid proteins just considered that the hybrid is functionally superior to the "pure" protein types. It seems, nevertheless, reasonable to suggest that hybrid proteins are sometimes of advantage to the organism carrying them. If hybrid proteins form any part of the explanation of heterosis they must quite often be advantageous. It is, however, impossible at present to give any direct evidence in support of this notion so far as interactions between "wild-type" alleles are concerned. The best one can do is to point out cases of regularly heteromultimeric proteins, which are undoubtedly of functional significance, and which *may* have had their origin in casual interaction between alleles.

An outstanding case in point is lactic dehydrogenase of mammals and birds. In a wide range of species this enzyme has been shown to occur in five isozymic forms. The explanation for this has been provided by Kaplan and his group (Fondy *et al.*, 1964). The molecules of the enzyme each contain four polypeptide chains of two interchangeable electrophoretically distinct kinds. One kind (H) predominates in heart muscle and the other (M) in skeletal muscle. In each tissue the pure tetramers H_4 and M_4 are accompanied by three kinds of mixed tetramer of different compositions—H_3M, H_2M_2, HM_3—in relative amounts depending on the overall ratio of H to M chains. The fact that the H and M chains are interchangeable in the enzyme structure suggests that they must have much in common, and they certainly have very similar molecular weights of about 37,000. Their amino acid compositions, however, are considerably different. Peptide mapping (fingerprinting) in two dimensions by paper chromatography and electrophoresis showed that at least 10 out of about 30 tryptic peptides are different in the two chains. The other 20 are not necessarily identical, but the fact that they coincide or overlap on fingerprints suggests that there may be substantial amino acid sequences in common. In sum, the evidence suggests considerable evolutionary divergence of originally homologous polypeptide chains.

The probable physiological significance of the existence of the two kinds of lactic dehydrogenase subunit has been shown by Wilson, Kahn, and Kaplan (1963). The H_4 enzyme is strongly inhibited by low concentrations of pyruvate while the M_4 enzyme is not. This suggests that the H_4 enzyme is more adapted to continuous muscular activity, like that of the heart, in which it is important that pyruvate be oxidized as it is formed, and not converted to lactic acid by the action of lactic dehydrogenase. The M_4 enzyme, on the other hand, seems well suited for muscle which is used for heavy but intermittent work. During a phase of work pyruvate can be produced faster than it can be oxidized and temporarily converted to lactic acid, which can then be oxidized during a subsequent rest period. This interpretation was supported by a survey of the lactic dehydrogenase types present in the wing muscle of a wide range of birds. The H_4 enzyme was found to predominate in birds which spend much time in continuous flight, such as certain sea birds and hawks, while the M_4 enzyme was the major component in the wing muscle of heavy land birds which fly only for short periods. The functional significance, if any, of the three hybrid enzyme types, is not so clear. No qualitatively new property appears on hybridization, so far as is known; the three different hybrids seem to form a nicely graded series, partaking of the properties of the two homomultimers to different extents, depending on the proportions of the two kinds of chain. It may be that an intermediate degree of pyruvate inhibition is just what is needed in certain tissues. On the other hand, it is conceivable that the presence of hybrids is an unavoidable and not significantly disadvantageous consequence of having two polypeptide chains which have diverged sufficiently to have different physiological functions but not enough to be mutually exclusive in multimers. However, the fact that the 5 lactate dehydrogenase isozymes occur in such a wide variety of mammals and birds indicates that the situation is evolutionarily extremely ancient and stable, and this is hard to understand if the heteromultimers have no functional advantages of their own.

Though it is attractive to think that the H and M chains had a common evolutionary origin, there is no doubt that they are now controlled by different genes. The evidence for this comes from the study of genetic variants of the two chains. In mice, Shaw and Barto (1963) showed that a genetic difference which altered the electrophoretic mobility of one chain had no effect on the other; an individual could be heterozygous with respect to a pair of alleles determining two different varieties of one chain while producing only the normal form of the other. Subsequently Kraus and Neely (1964) have made observations along similar lines in man. They distinguished four electrophoretic variants, three in the one kind of chain and one in the other.

Also very relevant to the argument are the very detailed studies which have been made on the structure of human hemoglobin. The complete amino acid sequences of the alpha and beta chains of the major adult hemoglobin (A) have been worked out (Braunitzer *et al.*, 1961; Konigsberg, Goldstein, and Hill, 1963), and so have the sequences of the gamma chain, which occurs in place of the beta chain in fetal hemoglobin (Schroeder *et al.*, 1963) and the delta chain, which occurs in place of the beta chain in the minor hemoglobin component A_2 (Ingram and Stretton, 1962). The alpha and beta chains differ extensively in their amino acid sequences, and they do not even have the same number of amino acid residues; alpha has 141 and beta 146. However, by lining the two sequences up side by side, and making two short gaps in the beta sequence and one in the alpha sequence, 61 amino acid residues can be seen to match in the two chains. The resemblance between the two sequences is most pronounced at the C-terminal end; comparing the two chains residue by residue from this end, 41 of the first 87 residues are the same. This is too great a resemblance to be fortuitous, and as Ingram (1961, 1962) has suggested, it may well be that the two chains have diverged in evolution from one ancestral type. When one compares the beta and gamma sequences the resemblance is much closer. Both these chains have 146 residues, and 104 of the amino acids are the same in each. The beta and delta chains are still more closely similar, with perhaps no more than eight amino acid differences. Studies of genetic variants have shown that the four kinds of chain are structurally determined by four different genes (see review by Baglioni, 1963). All, according to Ingram's hypothesis, may have arisen by duplication and subsequent divergence from a common ancestral gene.

As has been suggested by Partridge and Giles (1963), it is possible to regard hybrid proteins formed by fortuitous interaction of alleles as representing the first steps along the evolutionary road leading to proteins of the types exemplified by lactic dehydrogenase and hemoglobin. The situation may often arise that a heteropolymeric protein, formed as a result of the fortuitous coming together of slightly different alleles in a heterozygote, may be somewhat more advantageous to the organism than the homomultimer formed by either homozygote. This will then be a situation of heterosis through interallelic complementation. If the superiority of the heteromultimer is strong there will be a selective advantage in a genetic duplication which will enable both of the originally allelic genes to be carried in the same genome. Such a development would bring about a state of *permanent hybridity*, to use Darlington's (1958) phase. Instead of the two genetic components of the heteromultimer being segregated from each other at every meiosis, with the consequent formation of the two homozygous types in every generation, they would be carried together through the entire sexual cycle without segregation. Given enough time one would expect any strongly advantageous heteromultimer to become stabilized in this way, even though fortuitous duplication of the relevant genetic segment would be a rare event.

Once the duplication had occurred the functions of the duplicate genes would probably diverge progressively. Already to some extent complementary in function, further mutations making their complementation more efficient would tend to be selected. In course of time the two types of polypeptide chain might show only traces of their common origin. In the early stages of divergence multimers containing different proportions of the two chains might well be formed, and in some cases, where there was some special functional reason for being able to form several varieties of the same enzyme, this situation might persist indefinitely. This could give something

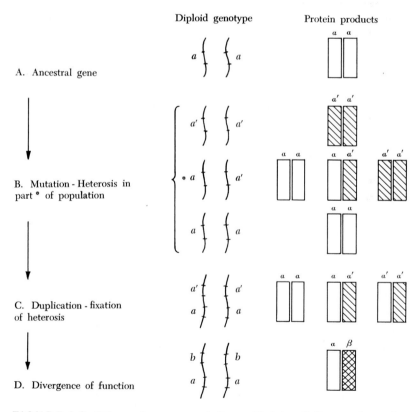

FIGURE 6-2   Scheme for gene evolution, with interallelic complementation as a transitional stage. The protein gene product is assumed here to be a dimer.

like the observed lactate dehydrogenase situation. More commonly, perhaps, the divergence of the two chains would result in a hetero-multimer of constant composition being formed in preference to any other possible multimer; in other words, the two kinds of subunit would no longer be structurally interchangeable. This is the hemoglobin situation. It is interesting to note, however, that where the production of the alpha chain of hemoglobin fails, as in certain forms of thalassemia (Baglioni, 1963), tetramers containing only beta chains (i.e., hemoglobin H) can be formed, indicating some degree of structural interchangeability even at such an advanced stage of divergence.

It will be appreciated that there are many gaps in the evidence supporting these speculations, which are summarized in Figure 6-2. In particular, complementation, in the very clear sense in which the term applies to interactions between functionally defective laboratory mutant alleles, has hardly been demonstrated at any stage of the postulated evolutionary process. The complementation involved here probably consists in a slight functional advantage of a heteromultimer over two functional homomultimers. Such an advantage might be critical from the point of view of natural selection and still be quite hard to demonstrate experimentally.

REFERENCES

Ahmad, M. and Catcheside, D. G. (1960). Physiological diversity among tryptophan synthetase mutants in *Neurospora crassa. Heredity,* **15**, 55.

Ahmed, A., Case, M. E., and Giles, N. H. (1964). The nature of complementation among mutants in the *histidine-3* region of *Neurospora crassa. Brookhaven Symp. in Biol.,* **17**, 53.

Allen, S. L., Misch, M. S., and Morrison, B. M. (1963). Genetic control of an acid phosphatase in *Tetrahymena:* Formation of a hybrid enzyme. *Genetics,* **48**, 1635.

Ames, B. N. and Hartman, P. E. (1963). The histidine operon. *Cold Spring Harb. Symp. Quant. Biol.,* **28**, 349.

Anderson, T. F. (1958). Recombination and segregation in *Escherichia coli. Cold Spring Harb. Symp. Quant. Biol.,* **23**, 47.

Baglioni, C. (1963). Correlations between genetics and chemistry of human hemoglobins. In *Molecular Genetics* (J. H. Taylor, ed.), Part 1, p. 405, Academic Press, New York.

Barratt, R. W. (1961). Studies on gene-protein relations with glutamic dehydrogenase in *Neurospora crassa. Genetics,* **46**, 849.

Beadle, G. W. and Coonradt, V. L. (1944). Heterocaryosis in *Neurospora crassa. Genetics,* **29**, 291.

Beadle, G. W. and Tatum, E. L. (1945). Neurospora II. Methods of producing and detecting mutations concerned with nutritional requirements. *Amer. J. Bot.,* **32**, 62.

Beckman, L. and Johnson, F. M. (1964). Genetic variations of phosphatase in larvae of *Drosophila melanogaster. Nature,* **201**, 321.

Beckman, L. and Johnson, F. M. (1964). Variations in larval alkaline phosphatases controlled by *Aph* alleles in *Drosophila melanogaster. Genetics,* **19**, 829.

Beckwith, J. R. (1964). A deletion analysis of the *lac* operator region in *Escherichia coli. J. Mol. Biol.,* **8**, 427.

Benzer, S. (1955). Fine structure of a genetic region in bacteriophage. *Proc. Nat. Acad. Sci., Wash.,* **41**, 344.

Benzer, S. (1958). The elementary units of heredity. In *The Chemical Basis of Heredity* (W. D. McElroy and B. Glass, eds.), p. 70, Johns Hopkins Press, Baltimore.

Benzer, S. (1961). On the topography of genetic fine structure. *Proc. Nat. Acad. Sci., Wash.,* **47**, 403.

Bernstein, H., Denhardt, G. H., and Edgar, R. S. (1965). Intragenic complementation among temperature sensitive mutants of bacteriophage T4D. *Genetics,* **51**, 987.

Bernstein, H. and Miller, A. (1961). Complementation studies with isoleucine-valine mutants of *Neurospora crassa. Genetics,* **46**, 1039.

Bevan, E. A. and Woods, R. A. (1962). Complementation between adenine requiring mutants in yeast. *Heredity,* **17**, 141.

Bonner, D. M. (1950). The Q locus of *Neurospora. Genetics,* **35**, 655.

Bonner, D. M. (1963). Gene enzyme relationships. *Proc. XI Int. Congr. Genetics (The Hague),* **2**, 141.

Braunitzer, G., Gehring-Muller, R., Hillschmann, N., Hilse, K., Hobam, G., Rudloff, V., and Wittman–Liebold, B. (1961). Amino acid sequence of the alpha chain of human hemoglobin. *Z. physiol. Chem. Hoppe-Seyler's,* **325**, 283.

Brenner, S. (1959). The mechanism of gene action. In *Symp. on Biochemistry of Human Genetics* (G. E. W. Wolstenholme and C. M. O'Connor, eds.), p. 304. Ciba Foundation and Intern. Union of Biol. Sciences, Churchill, London.

Brockman, H. E. and De Serres, F. J. (1963). Induction of *ad-3* mutants of *Neurospora crassa* by 2-aminopurine. *Genetics,* **48**, 597.

Bryan, C. R. and Miller, W. J. (1953). Interaction between alleles affecting cellular antigens following a species cross in Columbidae. *Proc. Nat. Acad. Sci., Wash.,* **39**, 412.

Cairns, J. (1963). The chromosome of *Escherichia coli. Cold Spring Harb. Symp. Quant. Biol.,* **28**, 43.

Carlson, E. A. (1959a). Allelism, complementation and pseudoallelism at the *dumpy* locus in *Drosophila melanogaster. Genetics,* **44**, 347.

Carlson, E. A. (1959b). Comparative genetics of complex loci. *Quart. Rev. Biol.,* **34**, 33.

Carsiotis, M., Appela, E., and Suskind, S. R. (1963). Purification and properties of tryptophan synthetase from *Neurospora crassa. Proc. XI Int. Congr. Genetics (The Hague),* **1**, 52.

Case, M. E. and Giles, N. H. (1960). Comparative complementation and genetic maps of the *pan-2* locus in *Neurospora crassa. Proc. Nat. Acad. Sci., Wash.,* **46**, 659.

Casselton, L. A. (1965). The production and behaviour of diploids of *Coprinus lagopus. Genet. Res., Camb.,* **6**, 190.

Catcheside, D. G. (1960). Complementation among histidine mutants of *Neurospora crassa. Proc. Roy. Soc. (London),* B**153**, 179.

Catcheside, D. G. (1965). Multiple enzymic functions of a gene in *Neurospora crassa. Biochem. Biophys. Res. Comm.,* **18**, 648.

Catcheside, D. G. and Overton, A. (1958). Complementation between alleles in heterocaryons. *Cold Spring Harb. Symp. Quant. Biol.,* **23**, 137.

Chilson, D. P., Costello, L. A., and Kaplan, N. D. (1965). Studies on the mechanism of hybridization of lactic dehydrogenase *in vitro. Biochemistry,* **4**, 271.

Chóvnick, A., Schalet, A., Kernaghan, R. P., and Kraus, M. (1964). The *rosy* cistron of *Drosophila melanogaster:* genetic fine structure analysis. *Genetics,* **50**, 1245.

Coddington, A. (1963). Quoted in *44th John Innes Institute Ann. Rept.,* p. 8.

Coddington, A. and Fincham, J. R. S. (1965). Proof of hybrid protein formation in a case of inter-allelic complementation in *Neurospora crassa. J. Mol. Biol.,* **12**, 152.

Cohn, M. (1957). Contributions of studies on the β-galactosidase of *E. coli* to our understanding of enzyme synthesis. *Bacteriol. Rev.,* **21**, 140.

Costello, W. P. and Bevan, E. A. (1964). Complementation between *ad-5/7* alleles in yeast. *Genetics,* **50**, 1219.

Craven, G. R., Steers, E., Jr., and Anfinsen, C. B. (1965). Purification, composition and molecular weight of the β-galactosidase of *Escherichia coli* K12. *J. Biol. Chem.,* **240**, 2468.

Crawford, I. P. and Yanofsky, C. (1958). On the separation of the tryptophan synthetase of *Escherichia coli* into two protein components. *Proc. Nat. Acad. Sci., Wash.,* **44**, 1161.

Cribbs, R. and Englesberg, E. (1964). L-Arabinose negative mutants of the L-ribulokinase structural gene affecting the levels of L-arabinose isomerase in *Escherichia coli. Genetics,* **49**, 95.

Crick, F. H. C. and Orgel, L. E. (1964). The theory of inter-allelic complementation. *J. Mol. Biol.,* **8**, 161.

Czerlinski, G. H. and Schreck, G. (1964). Fluorescence detection of the chemical relaxation of the reaction of lactate dehydrogenase with reduced nicotinamide adenine dinucleotide. *J. Biol. Chem.,* **239**, 913.

Darlington, C. D. (1958). *The Evolution of Genetic Systems,* 2nd ed, 265 pp., Oliver & Boyd, Edinburgh.

Davis, R. H. and Woodward, V. W. (1962). The relationship between gene suppression and aspartate transcarbamylase activity in *pyr-3* mutants of *Neurospora. Genetics,* **47**, 1075.

Demerec, M., Blomstrand, I., and Demerec, Z. E. (1955). Evidence of complex loci in *Salmonella. Proc. Nat. Acad. Sci., Wash.,* **41**, 359.

Demerec, M. and Hartman, P. E. (1959). Complex loci in microorganisms. *Ann. Rev. Microbiol.,* **13**, 377.

De Serres, F. J. (1956). Studies with purple adenine mutants in *Neurospora crassa.* I. Structural and functional complexity in the *ad-3* region. *Genetics,* **41**, 668.

De Serres, F. J. (1960). Studies with purple adenine mutants in Neurospora crassa. IV. Lack of complementation between different *ad-3A* mutants in heterocaryons and pseudowild types. *Genetics,* **45**, 555.

De Serres, F. J. (1962). Heterokaryon-incompatibility factor interaction in tests between *Neurospora* mutants. *Science,* **138**, 1342.

De Serres, F. J. (1963). Studies with purple adenine mutants in *Neurospora crassa.* V. Evidence for allelic complementation among *ad-3B* mutants. *Genetics,* **48**, 351.

Donachie, W. D. (1964). The regulation of pyrimidine biosynthesis in Neurospora crassa. II. Heterokaryons and the role of the "regulatory mechanisms." *Biochim. Biophys. Acta,* **82**, 293.

Dorfman, B. (1964). Allelic complementation at the *ad-5/7* locus in yeast. *Genetics,* **50**, 1231.

Dorn, G. L. and Burdick, A. B. (1962). On the recombinational structure and complementation relationships in the *m-dy* complex of *Drosophila melanogaster. Genetics,* **47**, 503.

Dua, R. D. and Burris, R. H. (1963). Stability of nitrogen-fixing enzymes and the reactivation of a cold labile enzyme. *Proc. Nat. Acad. Sci., Wash.,* **50**, 169.

Dubinin, N. P. (1932a). Step-allelomorphism in *Drosophila melanogaster.* The allelomorphs *achaete²-scute¹⁰, achaete¹-scute⁴,* and *achaete³-scute¹³. J. Genetics,* **25**, 163.

Dubinin, N. P. (1932b). Step-allelomorphism and the theory of centres of the gene *achaete-scute. J. Genetics,* **26**, 37.

Dubinin, N. P. (1933). Step-allelomorphism in *Drosophila melanogaster. J. Genetics,* **27**, 443.

East, E. M. (1936). Heterosis. *Genetics,* **21**, 375.

Edgar, R. S., Denhardt, G. H., and Epstein, R. H. (1964). A comparative genetic study of conditional lethal mutations of bacteriophage T4D. *Genetics,* **45**, 635.

Emerson, S. (1948). A physiological basis for some suppressor mutations and possibly for one gene heterosis. *Proc. Nat. Acad. Sci., Wash.,* **34**, 72.

Englesberg, E. (1961). Enzymatic characterization of 17 L-Arabinose negative mutants of *Escherichia coli. J. Bacteriol.,* **81**, 996.

Englesberg, E., Anderson, R., Weinberg, R., Lee, N., Hoffee, P., Huttenhauer, G., and Boyer, H. (1962). L-Arabinose sensitive, L-ribulose-5-phosphate 4-epimerase deficient mutants of *Escherichia coli. J. Bacteriol.,* **84**, 137.

Epstein, R. H., Bolle, A., Steinberg, C. M., Kellenberger, E., de la Tour, E. B., Chevalley, R., Edgar, R. M., Susman, M., Denhardt, G. H., and Lielausis, A. (1963). Physiological studies of conditional lethal mutants of bacteriophage T4D. *Cold Spring Harb. Symp. Quant. Biol.,* **28**, 375.

Fahmy, O. G. and Fahmy, M. J. (1959). Complementation among the sub-genic mutants in the *r*-locus of *Drosophila melanogaster. Nature,* **184**, 1927.

Fincham, J. R. S. (1957). A modified glutamic dehydrogenase as a result of gene mutation in *Neurospora crassa. Biochem. J.,* **65**, 721.

Fincham, J. R. S. (1958). The role of chromosomal loci in enzyme formation. *Proc. X Int. Congr. Genetics (Montreal),* **I**, 355, Univ. of Toronto Press, Toronto.

Fincham, J. R. S. (1959). On the nature of the glutamic dehydrogenase produced by inter-allelic complementation at the *am* locus of *Neurospora crassa. J. Gen. Microbiol.,* **21**, 600.

Fincham, J. R. S. (1960). Genetically controlled differences in enzyme activity. *Adv. Enzymol.,* **22**, 1.

Fincham, J. R. S. (1962). Genetically determined multiple forms of glutamic dehydrogenase in *Neurospora crassa. J. Mol. Biol.,* **4**, 257.

Fincham, J. R. S. and Bond, P. A. (1960). A further genetic variety of glutamic acid dehydrogenase in *Neurospora crassa. Biochem. J.,* **77**, 96.

Fincham, J. R. S. and Coddington, A. (1963a). Complementation at the *am* locus of *Neurospora crassa:* a reaction between different mutant forms of glutamate dehydrogenase. *J. Mol. Biol.,* **6**, 361.

Fincham, J. R. S. and Coddington, A. (1963b). The mechanism of complementation between *am* mutants of *Neurospora crassa. Cold Spring Harb. Symp. Quant. Biol.,* **28**, 517.

Fincham, J. R. S. and Day, P. R. (1965). *Fungal Genetics,* 2nd ed., 300 pp., Blackwell Scientific Publ., Oxford.

Fincham, J. R. S. and Pateman, J. A. (1957). Formation of an enzyme through complementary action of mutant "alleles" in separate nuclei in a heterocaryon. *Nature,* **179**, 741.

Fincham, J. R. S. and Stadler, D. R. (1965). Complementation relationships of Neurospora *am* mutants in relation to their formation of abnormal mutant varieties of glutamate dehydrogenase. *Genet. Res., Camb.,* **6**, 121.

Finger, I. and Heller, C. (1963). Immunogenetic analysis of proteins of paramecium. IV. Evidence for the presence of hybrid antigens in heterozygotes. *J. Mol. Biol.,* **6**, 190.

Fisher, H. F., McGregor L. L., and Cross, D. D. (1962a). The role of tyrosyl hydrogen bonds in the quaternary structure of the glutamate dehydrogenase molecule. *Biochim. Biophys. Acta,* **65**, 75.

Fisher, H. F., McGregor, L. L., and Power, U. (1962b). The nature of the alkaline dissociation of the glutamic dehydrogenase molecule. *Biochem. Biophys. Res. Comm.,* **8**, 402.

Fondy, T. P., Pesce, A., Freedberg, I., Solzenbach, F., and Kaplan, N. O. (1964). The comparative enzymology of lactic dehydrogenases. II. Properties of the crystalline HM₃ hybrid from chicken muscle and of H_2M_2 hybrid and H₄ enzyme from chicken liver. *Biochemistry,* **3**, 522.

Garen, A. and Echols, H. (1962). Genetic control of induction of alkaline phosphatase synthesis in *Escherichia coli. Proc. Nat. Acad. Sci., Wash.,* **48**, 1398.

Garen, A. and Garen, S. (1963). Complementation *in vivo* between structural mutants of alkaline phosphatase from *E. coli. J. Mol. Biol.,* **7**, 13.

Garnjobst, L. (1953). Genetic control of heterocaryosis in *Neurospora crassa. Amer. J. Bot.,* **40**, 607.

Garnjobst, L. (1955). Further analysis of genetic control of heterocaryosis in *Neurospora crassa. Amer. J. Bot.,* **42**, 444.

Garnjobst, L. and Wilson, J. F. (1956). Heterocaryosis and protoplasmic incompatibility in *Neurospora crassa. Proc. Nat. Acad. Sci., Wash.,* **42**, 613.

Giles, N. H. (1951). Studies on the mechanism of reversion in biochemical mutants of *Neurospora crassa. Cold Spring Harb. Symp. Quant. Biol.,* **16**, 283.

Giles, N. H. (1965). Genetic fine structure in relation to function in Neurospora. *Genetics Today,* **2**, 17 (*Proc. XI Int. Congr. Genetics*), S. J. Geerts, ed., Pergamon Press, Oxford.

Giles, N. H., Partridge, C. W. H., and Nelson, N. J. (1957). Genetic control of adenylosuccinase in *Neurospora crassa. Proc. Int. Genetics Symposia 1956,* (Suppl. to *Cytologia*), 543.

Glassman, E. (1962). Complementation between non-allelic *Drosophila* mutants deficient in xanthine dehydrogenase. *Proc. Nat. Acad. Sci., Wash.,* **48**, 1491.

Glassman, E. and Pinkerton, W. (1960). Complementation at the *maroon-like* eye color locus of *Drosophila melanogaster. Science,* **131**, 1810.

Gowen, J. W., ed. (1952). *Heterosis,* pp. 552 + ix, Iowa State College Press, Ames, Iowa.

Green, M. M. (1955). Pseudoallelism and the gene concept. *Amer. Nat.,* **89**, 65.

Green, M. M. (1959). Spatial and functional properties of pseudoalleles at the *white* locus in *Drosophila melanogaster. Heredity,* **13**, 303.

Green, M. M. (1961a). Phenogenetics of the *lozenge* loci in *Drosophila melanogaster.* II. Genetics of *lozenge-Krivchenko (lzᵏ). Genetics,* **46**, 1170.

Green, M. M. (1961b). Complementation at the *yellow* locus in *Drosophila melanogaster. Genetics,* **46**, 1385.

Green, M. M. (1963). Pseudoalleles and recombination in *Drosophila.* In *Methodology in Basic Genetics* (W. J. Burdette, ed.), Holden-Day, Inc., San Francisco.

Green, M. M. and Green, K. C. (1949). Crossing-over between alleles at the *lozenge* locus in *Drosophila melanogaster. Proc. Nat. Acad. Sci., Wash.,* **35**, 586.

Green, M. M. and Green, K. C. (1956). A cytogenetic analysis of the *lozenge* pseudoalles in *Drosophila. Z. für Vererbungs.,* **87**, 708.

Gross, J. and Englesberg, E. (1959). Determination of the order of mutational sites governing L-arabinose utilization in *Escherichia coli* B/r by transduction with phage Plb. *Virology,* **9**, 314.

Gross, S. R. (1962). On the mechanism of complementation at the *leu-2* locus of Neurospora. *Proc. Nat. Acad. Sci., Wash.,* **48**, 922.

Gross, S. R. and Gross, H. S. (1961). Some features of complementation at the *leucine-4* locus of Neurospora. *Genetics,* **46**, 868.

Gross, S. R. and Webster, R. E. (1963). Some aspects of inter-allelic complementation involving leucine biosynthetic enzymes of Neurospora. *Cold Spring Harb. Symp. Quant. Biol.,* **28**, 543.

Guidotti, G., Konigsberg, W., and Craig, L. C. (1963). On the dissociation of normal adult human hemoglobin. *Proc. Nat. Acad. Sci., Wash.,* **50**, 774.

Gutz, H. (1963). Untersuchungen zur Feinstruktur der Gene *ad₇* und *ad₆* von *Schizosaccharomyces pombe* Lind. Habilitationsschrift, Technischen Universität, Berlin.

Harris, I., Meriwether, B. P., and Park, J. H. (1963). Chemical nature of the catalytic sites in glyceraldehyde 3-phosphate dehydrogenase. *Nature,* **198**, 154.

Hartman, P. E., Hartman, Z., and Serman, D. (1960). Complementation mapping by abortive transduction of histidine requiring mutants. *J. Gen. Microbiol.,* **22**, 354.

Hartman, P. E., Loper, J. C., and Serman, D. (1960). Fine structure mapping by complete transduction between histidine-requiring Salmonella mutants. *J. Gen. Microbiol.,* **22**, 323.

Hass, L. F. (1964). Aldolase dissociation into sub-units by reaction with succinic anhydride. *Biochemistry,* **3**, 535.

Hass, L. F. and Lewis, M. S. (1963). Alkali-induced structural changes in muscle aldolase. *Biochemistry,* **2**, 1368.

Hawthorne, D. C. and Friis, J. (1964). Osmotic-remedial mutants. A new classification for nutritional mutants in yeast. *Genetics,* **50**, 829.

Hayashi, K., Hamaguchi, K., and Funatsu, M. (1963). Heat inactivation of muramidase. *J. Biochem.,* **53**, 374.

Hayes, W. (1964). *The Genetics of Bacteria and Their Viruses.* 740 pp., Blackwell Scientific Publ., Oxford.

Helling, R. B. and Weinberg, R. (1963). Complementation studies of arabinose genes in *Escherichia coli. Genetics,* **48,** 1397.

Holliday, R. (1961). Induced mitotic crossing-over in *Ustilago maydis. Genet. Res., Camb.,* **2,** 231.

Horne, R. W. and Greville, G. D. (1963). Observations on ox-liver L-glutamate dehydrogenase with the electron microscope. *J. Mol. Biol.,* **6,** 506.

Horowitz, N. H., Fling, M., MacLeod, H., and Sueoka, N. (1961). A genetic study of two new structural forms of tyrosinase in Neurospora. *Genetics,* **46,** 1015.

Hull, F. H. (1952). Recurrent selection and overdominance. In *Heterosis* (J. W. Gowen, ed), p. 451, Iowa State College Press, Ames, Iowa.

Ingram, V. M. (1961). Gene evolution and the haemoglobins. *Nature,* **189,** 704.

Ingram, V. M. (1962). The evolution of a protein. *Fed. Proc.,* **21,** 1053.

Ingram, V. M. and Stretton, A. O. W. (1962). Human haemoglobin A$_2$ II. The chemistry of some peptides peculiar to haemoglobin A$_2$. *Biochim. Biophys. Acta,* **63,** 20.

Irwin, M. R. (1951). Genetics and immunology. In *Genetics in the 20th Century* (L. C. Dunn, ed.), 634 pp., Macmillan, New York.

Irwin, M. R. and Cumley, R. W. (1945). Suggestive evidence for duplicate genes in a species hybrid in doves. *Genetics,* **30,** 363.

Ishikawa, T. (1962a). Genetic studies of *ad-8* mutants in Neurospora crassa. I. Genetic fine structure of the *ad-8* locus. *Genetics,* **47,** 1147.

Ishikawa, T. (1962b). Genetic studies of *ad-8* mutants in *Neurospora crassa.* II. Interallelic complementation at the *ad-8* locus. *Genetics,* **47,** 1755.

Ishikawa, T. (1965). A molecular model for an enzyme based on the genetic and complementation analyses at the *ad-8* locus in *Neurospora. J. Mol. Biol.,* **13,** 586.

Jacob, F. and Monod, J. (1961a). Genetic regulatory mechanisms in the synthesis of proteins. *J. Mol. Biol.,* **3,** 318.

Jacob, F. and Monod, J. (1961b). On the regulation of gene activity. *Cold Spring Harb. Symp. Quant. Biol.,* **26,** 193.

Jacob, F. and Wollman, E. L. (1961). *Sexuality and the Genetics of Bacteria,* 374 pp., Academic Press, New York and London.

Jirgensons, B. (1961). Glutamic acid dehydrogenase—a protein of unusual conformation. *J. Amer. Chem. Soc.,* **83,** 3161.

Johnson, F. M. and Denniston, C. (1964). Genetic variation of alcohol dehydrogenase in *Drosophila melanogaster. Nature,* **204,** 907.

Johnson, F. M. and Sakai, R. K. (1964). A leucine aminopeptidase polymorphism in *Drosophila buskii. Nature,* **203,** 373.

Jones, D. F. (1917). Dominance of linked factors as a means of accounting for heterosis. *Genetics,* **2,** 462.

Kaplan, S., Suyama, Y., and Bonner, D. M. (1964). Fine structure genetic analysis at the *td* locus of *Neurospora crassa. Genetics,* **49,** 145.

Kapuler, A. M. and Bernstein, H. (1963). A molecular model for an enzyme based on a correlation between the genetic and complementation maps of the locus specifying the enzyme. *J. Mol. Biol.,* **6,** 443.

Konigsberg, W., Goldstein, J., and Hill, R. J. (1963). The structure of human hemoglobin VII. The digestion of the β-chain of human hemoglobin with pepsin. *J. Biol. Chem.,* **238,** 2028.

Koorajian, S. and Zabin, I. (1965). Carboxypeptidase studies on β-galactosidase: detection of one C-terminal lysine per monomer. *Biochem. Biophys. Res. Comm.*, **18**, 384.

Koshland, D. E., Jr. (1960). The active site and enzyme action. *Advances Enzymol.*, **22**, 45.

Kraus, A. P. and Neely, C. L., Jr. (1964). Human erythrocyte lactate dehydrogenase: four genetically determined variants. *Science*, **145**, 595.

Labouesse, B., Hairsteen, B. H., and Hess, G. P. (1962). Conformational changes in enzyme catalysis. *Proc. Nat. Acad. Sci., Wash.*, **48**, 2137.

Lacy, A. M. and Bonner, D. M. (1962). Complementation between alleles at the *td* locus in *Neurospora crassa*. *Proc. Nat. Acad. Sci., Wash.*, **47**, 72.

Laughnan, J. R. (1948). The action of allelic forms of the gene A in maize. I. Studies of variability, dosage and dominance relations. The divergent character of the series. *Genetics*, **33**, 488.

Laughnan, J. R. (1949). The action of allelic forms of the gene A in maize. II. The relation to crossing over to mutation of A^b. *Proc. Nat. Acad. Sci. Wash.*, **35**, 167.

Laughnan, J. R. (1952). The action of allelic forms of the gene A in maize. IV. On the compound nature of A^b and the occurrence and action of its A^d derivatives. *Genetics*, **37**, 375.

Lederberg, J. (1949). Aberrant heterozygotes in *Escherichia coli*. *Proc. Nat. Acad. Sci., Wash.*, **35**, 178.

Lederberg, J. (1957). Sibling recombinants in zygote pedigrees of *Escherichia coli*. *Proc. Nat. Acad. Sci., Wash.*, **43**, 1060

Lee, N. and Englesberg, E. (1963). Co-ordinate variation in induced synthesis of enzyme associated with mutation in a structural gene. *Proc. Nat. Acad. Sci., Wash.*, **50**, 696.

Leupold, U. (1955). Methodisches zur Genetik von *Schizosaccharomyces pombe*. *Schweiz. Z. Allg. Path. Bakt.*, **18**, 1141.

Leupold, U. and Gutz, H. (1965). Genetic fine structure in *Schizosaccharomyces*. *Genetics Today*, **2**, 31 (*Proc. XI Int. Congr. Genetics*), S. J. Geerts, ed., Pergamon Press, Oxford.

Lewis, E. B. (1945). The relation of repeats to position effect in *Drosophila melanogaster*. *Genetics*, **30**, 137.

Lewis, E. B. (1951). Pseudoallelism and gene evolution. *Cold Spring Harb. Symp. Quant. Biol.*, **16**, 159.

Lewis, E. B. (1952). The pseudoallelism of *white* and *apricot* in *Drosophila melanogaster*. *Proc. Nat. Acad. Sci., Wash.*, **38**, 953.

Lewis, E. B. (1955). Some aspects of pseudoalleles. *Amer. Nat.*, **89**, 73.

Lewis, E. B. (1963). Genes and developmental pathways. *Amer. Zoologist*, **3**, 33.

Li, T.-K. and Vallee, B. L. (1964). Active center peptides of liver alcohol dehydrogenase I. The sequence surrounding the active cysteinyl residues. *Biochemistry*, **3**, 869.

Loper, J. C. (1961). Enzyme complementation in mixed extracts of mutants from the Salmonella *histidine B* locus. *Proc. Nat. Acad. Sci., Wash.*, **47**, 1440.

Lyon, M. F. (1963). Attempts to test the inactive-X theory of dosage compensation in mammals. *Genet. Res., Camb.*, **4**, 93.

Maas, W. K., Maas, R., Wiame, J. M., and Glansdorff, N. (1964). Studies on the mechanism of repression of arginine biosynthesis in *Escherichia coli*. I. Dominance of repressibility in zygotes. *J. Mol. Biol.*, **8**, 359.

McGibbon, W. H. (1944). Cellular antigens in species and species hybrids in ducks. *Genetics*, **29**, 407.

Markert, C. L. (1963). Lactate dehydrogenase isozymes: dissociation and recombination of subunits. *Science*, **140**, 1329.

Markham, R., Frey, S., and Hills, G. J. (1963). Methods of enhancement of image detail and accentuation of detail in electron microscopy. *Virology*, **20**, 88.

Massey, V., Hofmann, T., and Palmer, G. (1962). The relation of function and structure in lipoyl dehydrogenase. *J. Biol. Chem.*, **237**, 3820.

Matsushiro, A., Sato, K., and Kida, S. (1964). Characteristics of the transducing elements of bacteriophage φ80. *Virology*, **23**, 299.

Megnet, R. and Giles, N. H. (1964). Allelic complementation at the adenylo-succinate locus in *Schizosaccharomyces pombe*. *Genetics*, **50**, 967.

Monod, J., Changeux, J.-P., and Jacob, F. (1963). Allosteric proteins and cellular control systems. *J. Mol. Biol.*, **6**, 306.

Morgan, T. H., Sturtevant, A. H., Muller, H. J., and Bridges, C. B. (1915). *The Mechanisms of Mendelian Heredity*, 262 pp., Henry Holt & Co., New York.

Morgan, T. H. (1919). *The Physical Basis of Heredity*, 305 pp., J. P. Lippincott, Philadelphia and London.

Morse, M. L. (1959). Recombination and segregation in *gal* heterogenotes showing position effect. *Genetics*, **44**, 528.

Morse, M. L. and Lederberg, J. (1956). Transductional heterogenotes in *Escherichia coli*. *Genetics*, **41**, 758.

Murray, N. E. (1960). Complementation and recombination between *methionine-2* alleles in *Neurospora crassa*. *Heredity*, **15**, 207.

Ozeki, H. (1956). Abortive transduction in purine-requiring mutants of *Salmonella typhimurium*. *Carnegie Inst. Wash. Publ.*, **612**, 97.

Pardee, A. B., Jacob, F., and Monod, J. (1959). The genetic control and cytoplasmic expression of "inducibility" in the synthesis of β-galactosidase of *E. coli. J. Mol. Biol.*, **1**, 165.

Partridge, C. W. H. (1961). Altered properties of the enzyme, adenylosuccinase, produced by interallelic complementation at the *ad-4* locus in *Neurospora crassa*. *Biochem. Biophys. Res. Comm.*, **3**, 613.

Partridge, C. W. H. and Giles, N. H. (1963). Sedimentation behavior of adenylosuccinase formed by interallelic complementation in *Neurospora crassa*. *Nature*, **199**, 304.

Pateman, J. A. and Fincham, J. R. S. (1965). Complementation and enzyme studies on revertants induced in an *am* mutant of *N. crassa*. *Genet. Res., Camb.*, in press.

Perrin, D. (1963). Complementation between products of the β-galactosidase structural gene of *Escherichia coli*. *Cold Spring Harb. Symp. Quant. Biol.*, **28**, 529.

Pittenger, T. H. (1954). The general incidence of pseudo-wild wild types in *Neurospora crassa*. *Genetics*, **39**, 326.

Pittenger, Y. H., Kimball, A. W., and Atwood, K. C. (1955). Control of nuclear ratios in Neurospora heterokaryons. *Amer. J. Bot.*, **42**, 954.

Pontecorvo, G. (1950). New fields in the biochemical genetics of microorganisms. *Symp. Biochem. Soc. (London)*, **4**, 40.

Pontecorvo, G. (1959). *Trends in Genetic Analysis*, 145 pp., Oxford Univ. Press.

Pontecorvo, G. (1963). Microbial genetics: retrospect and prospect. *Proc. Roy. Soc. (London)* **B158**, 1.

Pontecorvo, G., Roper, J. A., Hemmons, L. M., MacDonald, K. D., and Bufton, A. W. J. (1953). The genetics of *Aspergillus nidulans. Adv. Genetics,* **5**, 141.

Pritchard, R. H. (1955). The linear arrangement of a series of alleles of *Aspergillus nidulans. Heredity,* **9**, 343.

Rachmeler, M. and Yanofsky, C. (1961). Biochemical, immunological and genetic studies with a new kind of tryptophan synthetase mutant of *Neurospora crassa. J. Bacteriol.,* **81**, 955.

Ramirez, C. Friis, J., and Leupold, U. (1963). Allelic recombination in adenine-requiring mutants of *Schizosaccharomyces pombe. Proc. XI Int. Congr. Genetics (The Hague),* **1**, 7.

Reissig, J. L. (1960). Forward and back mutation in the *pyr-3* region of Neurospora. I. Mutation from arginine dependence to prototrophy. *Genet. Res., Camb,* **1**, 356.

Reithel, F. J. (1963). The dissociation and association of protein structures. *Adv. Protein Chem.,* **18**, 123.

Roberts, D. B. (1964). Ph.D. dissertation, University of Cambridge.

Roberts, D. B. and Pateman, J. A. (1964). Immunological studies of amination deficient strains of *Neurospora crassa. J. Gen. Microbiol.,* **34**, 295.

Roper, J. A. (1950). Search for linkage between genes determining a vitamin requirement. *Nature,* **166**, 956.

Roper, J. A. (1952). Production of heterozygous diploids in filamentous fungi. *Experientia,* **8**, 14.

Roper, J. A. and Pritchard, R. H. (1955). Recovery of the complementary products of mitotic crossing-over. *Nature,* **175**, 639.

Rosenberg, A. and Lumry, R. (1964). The reversible transconformation processes in yeast enolase. *Biochemistry,* **3**, 1055.

Rothman, F. and Byrne, R. (1963). Fingerprint analysis of alkaline phosphatase of *Escherichia coli* K12. *J. Mol. Biol.,* **6**, 330.

Sarabhai, A. S., Stretton, A. O. W., Brenner, S., and Bolle, A. (1964). Co-linearity of the gene with the polypeptide chain. *Nature,* **201**, 13.

Scandalios, J. G. (1965). Subunit dissociation and recombination of catalase isozymes. *Proc. Nat. Acad. Sci., Wash.,* **53**, 1035.

Schalet, A., Kernaghan, R. P., and Chovnick, A. R. (1964). Structural and phenotypic definition of the *rosy* cistron in *Drosophila melanogaster. Genetics,* **50**, 1261.

Schlesinger, M. J. and Levinthal, C. (1963). Hybrid protein formation of *E. coli* alkaline phosphatase leading to *in vitro* complementation. *J. Mol. Biol.,* **7**, 1.

Schlesinger, M. J., Torriani, A., and Levinthal, C. (1963). *In vitro* formation of enzymically active hybrid proteins from *Escherichia coli* alkaline phosphatase CRM's. *Cold Spring Harb. Symp. Quant. Biol.,* **28**, 539.

Schroeder, W. A., Shelton, J. R., Shelton, J. B., Cormick, J., and Jones, R. T. (1963). The amino acid sequence of the γ chain of human fetal hemoglobin. *Biochemistry,* **2**, 92.

Schwartz, D. (1960). Genetic studies on mutant enzymes in maize: synthesis of hybrid enzymes by heterozygotes. *Proc. Nat. Acad. Sci., Wash.,* **46**, 1210.

Schwartz, D. (1962). Genetic studies on mutant enzymes in maize. II. On the mode of synthesis of the hybrid enzymes. *Proc. Nat. Acad. Sci., Wash.,* **48**, 750.

Schwartz, D. (1964). A second hybrid enzyme in maize. *Proc. Nat. Acad. Sci., Wash.,* **51**, 682.

Shaw, C. R. and Barto, E. (1963). Genetic evidence for the sub-unit structure of lactate dehydrogenase isozymes. *Proc. Nat. Acad. Sci., Wash.,* **50**, 211.

Stadler, L. J. (1946). Spontaneous mutation at the R locus in maize. I. The aleurone-color and plant-color effects. *Genetics,* **31**, 377.

Stadler, L. J. and Emmerling, M. H. (1945). Relation of unequal crossing over to the inter-dependence of R^r elements (P) and (S). *Genetics,* **41**, 124.

Stadler, L. J. and Fogel, S. (1945). Gene variability in maize. II. The action of certain R alleles. *Genetics,* **30**, 23.

Stahl, F. W., Edgar, R. S., and Steinberg, J. (1964). The linkage map of bacteriophage T4. *Genetics,* **50**, 539.

Steers, E., Jr., Craven, G. R., Anfinsen, C. B. and Bethune, J. L. (1965). Evidence for nonidentical subunits in the β-galactosidase of *Escherichia coli* K12. *J. Biol. Chem.,* **240**, 2478.

Stent, G. (1964). The operon: on its third anniversary. *Science,* **144**, 816.

Stocker, B. A. D. (1956). Abortive transduction of motility in *Salmonella;* a non-replicated gene transmitted through many generations to a single descendant. *J. Gen. Microbiol.,* **15**, 575.

Sundaram, T. K., and Fincham, J. R. S. (1964). A mutant glutamate dehydrogenase in Neurospora interconvertible between electrophoretically distinct active and inactive forms. *J. Mol. Biol.,* **10**, 423.

Suyama, Y. (1963). *In vitro* complementation in the tryptophan synthetase mutants of *Neurospora crassa. Biochem. Biophys. Res. Comm.,* **10**, 144.

Suyama, Y. and Bonner, D. M. (1962). Complementation, mutation and enzyme alteration in the tryptophan synthetase system of Neurospora. *Genetics,* **47**, 989.

Suyama, Y. and Bonner, D. M. (1964). Complementation between tryptophan synthetase mutants of *Neurospora crassa. Biochim. Biophys. Acta,* **81**, 565.

Suyama, Y., Munkres, K. D., and Woodward, V. W. (1959). Genetic analysis of the *pyr-3* locus of *Neurospora crassa;* the bearing of recombination and gene conversion upon intra-allelic linearity. *Genetica,* **30**, 293.

Tessman, I. (1965). Complementation groups in phage S13. *Virology,* **25**, 303.

Ullmann, A., Perrin, D., Jacob F. and Monod, J. (1965). Identification par complémentation *in vitro* et purification d'un segment peptidique de la β-galactosidase d'*Escherichia coli. J. Mol. Biol.,* **12**, 918.

Wallenfels, K., Sund, H., and Weber, K. (1963). Die untereinheiten der β-galactosidase aus *E. coli. Biochem. Z.,* **338**, 714.

Webber, B. B. (1960). Genetical and biochemical studies of histidine-requiring mutants of *Neurospora crassa.* II. Evidence concerning heterogeneity among *hist-3* mutants. *Genetics,* **45**, 1617.

Webber, B. B. and Case, M. E. (1960). Genetical and biochemical studies of histidine requiring mutants of *Neurospora crassa. Genetics,* **45**, 1605.

Welshons, W. J. and von Halle, E. S. (1962). Pseudoallelism at the *notch* locus in Drosophila. *Genetics,* **47**, 743.

Westhead, E. W. (1964). The reversible denaturation processes of yeast enolase. *Biochemistry,* **3**, 1062.

Whiting, P. W. (1951). Multiple complementary alleles in *Habrobracon* and *Mormoniella*. *J. Genetics*, **50**, 206.

Wilson, A. C., Kahn, R. D., and Kaplan, N. O. (1963). Functions of the two forms of lactic dehydrogenase in the breast muscle of birds. *Nature*, **197**, 331.

Winstead, J. A. and Wold, F. (1964). Studies on rabbit muscle enolase. Chemical evidence for two polypeptide chains in the active enzyme. *Biochemistry*, **3**, 791.

Woodward, D. O. (1959). Enzyme complementation *in vitro* between adenylo-succinase-less mutants of *Neurospora crassa*. *Proc. Nat. Acad. Sci.*, *Wash.*, **45**, 346.

Woodward, D. O., Partridge, C. W. H., and Giles, N. H. (1958). Complementation at the *ad-4* locus in *Neurospora crassa*. *Proc. Nat. Acad. Sci.*, *Wash.*, **44**, 1237.

Woodward, V. W. (1962). Complementation and recombination among *pyr-3* heteroalleles of *Neurospora crassa*. *Proc. Nat. Acad. Sci.*, *Wash.*, **48**, 348.

Yanofsky, C. (1960). The tryptophan synthetase system. *Bact. Rev.*, **24**, 221.

Yanofsky, C., Carlton, B. C., Guest, J. R., Helinski, D. R., and Henning, U. (1964). On the colinearity of gene structure and protein structure. *Proc. Nat. Acad. Sci.*, **51**, 266.

Yanofsky, C. and Crawford, I. P. (1959). The effects of deletions, point mutations, reversions and suppressor mutations on the two components of the tryptophan synthetase of *Escherichia coli*. *Proc. Nat. Acad. Sci.*, *Wash.*, **45**, 1016.

Young, W. J., Porter, J. E., and Childs, B. (1964). Glucose-6-phosphate dehydrogenase in Drosophila: X-linked electrophoretic variants. *Science*, **143**, 140.

Zabin, I. (1963). Proteins of the lactose system. *Cold Spring Harb. Symp. Quant. Biol.*, **28**, 431.

Zipser, D. (1963a). A study of the urea-produced sub-units of β-galactosidase. *J. Mol. Biol.*, **7**, 113.

Zipser, D. (1963b). Studies on the ribosome-bound β-galactosidase of *Escherichia coli*. *J. Mol. Biol.*, **7**, 739.

Zipser, D. and Perrin, D. (1963). Complementation on ribosomes. *Cold Spring Harb. Symp. Quant. Biol.*, **28**, 533.

INDEX

Abortive transduction (*see* Complementation tests)

Activation of conformationally abnormal proteins, 84

Adenylosuccinase, of *Neurospora*, 41, 48, 65, 68, 70
  of *Schizosaccharomyces*, 10

Adenylosuccinate synthetase, 108

Alcohol dehydrogenase, 66, 119–120

Aldolase, 66

Alkaline phosphatase, of *Drosophila* (*see Drosophila*)
  of *Escherichia coli*, 41, 66, 68, 71, 73, 89
    deficient mutants, 48, 71
    "fingerprinting" analysis, 41
    molecular weight, 41, 71
    subunits, 41, 71

Allele, 31

Allelic complementation (*see* Interallelic complementation)

Allosteric effector, 82

Allosteric transition, 82

Allostery, 81

Amber mutants, 92

Antigens, in birds, 115–118
  in *Paramecium*, 118
  (*see also* Hybrid proteins)

L-Arabinose isomerase, 52–53, 55

L-Arabinose permease, 52

Arabinose mutants (*see Escherichia coli*)

Arginine mutants (*see Escherichia coli, Neurospora crassa*)

Argininosuccinase of *Neurospora*, 41, 47

Ascomycetes, 35

Ascospores, 2
  diploid, 10

Aspartic transcarbamylase, 64

Aspergillus nidulans, 3
  ad-9 mutants, 97
  genetic fine structure, 26–28
  heterokaryons, 8–9, 18

Auxotrophic mutants, 2
  (*see also* names of organisms)

Axis of symmetry, 107, 109–112
  threefold, 109
  twofold, 109
  (*see also* Homologous correction)

Bacteriophage, PLT22 (P22), 14–15
  φ80, 13
  S13, 16
  T2, 16
  T4, 16–17, 89

host range, 17
rII mutants, 16, 27–30, 34, 36
temperature sensitive mutants, 16–17, 92–94, 97, 103–104, 106
temperate, 12
(*see also Amber* mutants and Lambda)
Basidiomycetes, 3

cis-trans position effect, 22–24, 27, 45, 55
cis-trans test, 29–30, 50
Cistron, 29–31, 33–34, 55
function, 30–31
Clamp connections, 3
Coenocytic fungi, 5–9
Complementation (*see* Incomplete, Interallelic, Intergenic, "Negative")
Complementation groups, 80
Complementation map, 34–37, 46, 57, 59, 61, 87, 90–112
comparison with genetic map, 103–107
cutoff points, 93, 103
different forms, 94–98
graded spreading effects in, 103
linearity, 109
meaning, 99–112
number of segments in, 96–98
of protein subunit, 99
rule for construction, 94
usefulness, 112
Complementation tests, 1–17
by abortive transduction, 14–15, 55
in *Aspergillus*, 8
in bacteria, 10–15
with dikaryons, 3–6
in diploids, 8–10, 20–22
with F′ episomes, 13–14
by heterokaryosis, 3–9, 22, 93
with merozygotes, 11
in *Neurospora*, 5–9
in T4 bacteriophage, 16–17, 29–30
in yeast, 2–3, 10
Conditional lethal mutants, 92, 94
Conformational abnormality in proteins, 83–89
correction of, 84–87

Conformation-correction hypothesis, 80–87, 100, 108, 110
Conidia, 4, 6
diploid, 9
heterokaryotic, 4
multinucleate, 4, 7
uninucleate, 7, 9
Constitutive mutants, 51
Coordinately controlled enzymes, 51–55
Coprinus lagopus, 3, 4, 10
Cross-reacting material (CRM), 56–57, 70
Cutoff points (*see* Complementation map)

Deletion mutants, 36, 43
(*see also* Overlapping deletions)
Dikaryons, 3–5, 10
Diploid, 1–3
partial, 10–15, 18
selection of in fungi, 9–10
Disomic, 8
Doves, 116–118
Drosophila buskii (*see* Leucine aminopeptidase)
Drosophila melanogaster, 19
alcohol dehydrogenase variants, 119–120
alkaline phosphatase variants, 119
glucose-6-phosphate dehydrogenase variants, 120, 121
mutants
asteroid (ast), 22–23, 25
bithorax, 55
dumpy (dy) series, 38–40, 47, 63
eye color, 20
forked (f), 25
garnet, 25
lozenge (lz), 24–25
maroon-like (ma-l), 47
miniature-dusky (m-dy) series, 45
notch (no), 25, 40
rosy, 25
rudimentary (r), 34–35
scute (sc), 34, 63
singed (sn), 25
Star (S), 22, 23, 25
stubble, 25
vermilion (v), 25

white (w) series, 20, 24–25
yellow (y), 34
xanthine dehydrogenase, 47
Duplication, 124, 125
Dyad axis, 109–111

Enolase, 66, 82
Enzyme (*see* names of individual enzymes)
Episome, 12, 13, 44, 48, 89
Escherichia coli, 11–14, 28
mutants,
    arabinose (ara), 12, 52–53
    arginine (arg), 12
    galactose (gal), 12
    lactose (lac), 12–13, 41, 50–52, 55
    p (phosphatase), 13, 41, 48, 68–72, 89
    tryptophan (*tryp*), 13
    y (permease), 51
    z (galactosidase), 41–45, 49, 52, 68–69, 79–80
    (*see also* Alkaline phosphatase F, F⁻, F⁺, F′, β-Galactosidase, Galactoside transacetylase, Tryptophan synthetase)

F (fertility) factor of *E. coli*, 11–13
F-minus (F⁻) strains of *E. coli*, 11, 13
F-plus (F⁺) strains of *E. coli*, 13
F-prime (F′) strains of *E. coli*, 13, 44, 48, 79, 89

β-Galactosidase of *E. coli*, 50–51, 68, 78–80
molecular weight, 41–42
omega peptide, 49
subunits, 42–43, 49, 78
β-Galactoside permease of *E. coli*, 50–51
β-Galactoside transacetylase of *E. coli*, 51
Gene, 19–32, 45, 50
Genome, 1
Glutamate dehydrogenase, of liver, 66, 109
of *Neurospora*, 42, 48, 63, 68, 71, 72, 76–78, 83–89, 99–100
molecular weight, 41–42, 74
subunits, 42, 74
Glyceraldehyde 3-phosphate dehydrogenase, 66

Habrobracon, 22
Haploid, 2
Haploidization, 9
Hemoglobin, 107
A, 123
A₂, 124
amino acid sequences, 123–124
electrophoretically distinct varieties, 121
fetal, 124
H, 126
hybrids, 121
partial homology of chains, 124
Heterogenote, 12, 44, 51, 69, 79
segregation in, 12
Heterokaryon, 3–9, 18
(*see also* Incompatibility, Nuclear ratio, and names of organisms)
Heteromultimers, 41, 49, 67, 80
evolutionary stabilization, 121–126
functional significance, 121–126
Heterosis, theories of, 113–115, 124–125
Heterothallism, 2
Hfr strains of *E. coli*, 11, 13
Histidinol dehydrogenase of *Neurospora*, 57–58
Homologous correction theory, 101–103, 108–111
Homomultimer, 67, 80
Hybrid enzymes shown by electrophoresis, 118–121
Hybrid proteins, antigens, 115–118
mechanisms of formation
    in vitro, 71–78
    in vivo, 78–80
Hybrid protein hypothesis, 65–69, 85–87, 99
Hymenomycetes, 3

Imidazoleglycerol phosphate dehydrase (of *Salmonella*), 68, 70
Incompatibility in heterokaryon formation, 5–6, 9
Incomplete complementation, 44–50, 58
Inducer, 51–52
Interallelic complementation, 31, 32, 44, 47–48
crossing-over hypothesis, 65, 99
depending on balance, 64

evolutionary significance, 113–126
general incidence, 90–92
giving new enzyme activity, 64–89
  in vitro, 43, 69–78, 85–86
    with ribosomes, 78–80
  in vivo, 70–71
  in vivo and *in vitro*, comparison of
    products, 69–72
  resulting from independent action
    of alleles, 62–64
  as a stage in protein evolution, 115,
    124–126
  (*see also* Hybrid protein hypothesis)
Intercistronic complementation (*see*
    Intergenic complementation)
Intergenic complementation, 32, 44,
    114
Intracistronic complementation (*see*
    Interallelic complementation)

Lactate dehydrogenase, 124
  isozymic forms, 122–123
  subunits, 122
Lactose (*lac*) mutants (*see Escherichia
    coli*)
Lambda bacteriophage, 12
  defective, 12
  induction by ultraviolet light, 12
Leucine aminopeptidase (of *Dro-
    sophila*), 120
Lipoyl dehydrogenase, 66
Locus, 32

Maize (*see Zea mays*)
Mating type, 2, 5, 10
Meiosis, 2, 3, 10
Merozygote, 11, 18
Messenger RNA, 51
Mice, 2
Michaelis constant, 63, 71, 72
Minimal medium, 2
Monokaryons, 3, 10
Monomeric proteins, 90
Mormoniella, 22
Multimeric proteins, 105–112
Multiple allelic series, 20
Muton, 29

"Negative" complementation, 87–89

Neurospora crassa, 3, 28
  auxotrophic mutants, 22
    adenine-3B (*ad-3B*), 91, 96
    ad-4, 33–34, 36, 41, 48, 65, 68,
      95–96
    ad-8, 36–38, 96, 105–108
    amination (*am*), 7, 33, 41–42, 48,
      65, 68–69, 71–72, 76–77, 82–
      89, 96, 99–100
    arginine-1 (*arg-1*), 7, 34, 35, 96
    arg-2, 64
    arg-10, 41
    histidine-1 (*hist-1*), 96
    hist-2, 96
    hist-3, 56–59, 96
    hist-5, 96
    hist-6, 91
    isoleucine-valine-2 (*iv-2*), 96
    iv-3, 96
    leucine-2 (*leu-2*), 95–96, 102
    leu-3, 102
    leu-4, 96
    methionine-2 (*me-2*), 96
    pantothenic acid-2 (*pan-2*), 34,
      36–38, 95–96
    pyrimidine-3 (*pyr-3*), 39, 58–59,
      64, 96
    sulfonamide-requiring (*sfo*), 64
    tryptophan-1 (*tryp-1*), 96
    tryp-3 (*td*), 36, 47, 56–57, 62–63,
      68, 70, 72, 96
  heterokaryons, 5–9, 47
  (*see also* Adenylosuccinase, Gluta-
    mate dehydrogenase, Histidi-
    nol dehydrogenase, Tryptophan
    synthetase)
Neurospora tetrasperma, 6
  (*see also* Secondary homothallism)
"Nonsense" mutations, 92
Nuclear ratios in heterokaryons, 6–9,
  18

Operator, 51
  mutants, 51–52, 55–56, 58, 60
Operon, 24, 26, 50, 51, 56, 58
  distinction from gene, 50–61
  in *Neurospora*, 58–59
Osmotically curable mutants, 92
Overdominance, 115
Overlapping deletions, 28

Paramecium aurelia, 118
Perithecium, 3
Permanent hybridity, 124
Phycomycetes, 5
Polarity mutants, 51–53, 55–56, 58, 60
Prophage, 12, 16
Prototroph, 10
Pseudoallelism, 24–26, 28–29, 55
Pseudowild types, in *Neurospora,* 8–9

rII mutants (*see* Bacteriophage T4)
Recon, 29
L-Ribulokinase (of *E. coli*), 52–53
L-Ribulose-5-phosphate 4-epimerase (of *E. coli*), 52–53, 55

Saccharomyces cerevisiae, 2, 28
  auxotrophic mutants,
    adenine-2 (*ad-2*), 97
    ad-5/7, 60, 94, 97
    (*see also* Osmotically curable mutants)
  complementation tests, 2, 3
  red adenine mutants, 2, 3
Salmonella typhimurium, 14, 15, 28
  histidine mutants, 15, 54–55, 68, 70, 91
  nonmotile mutants, 14
  (*see also* Abortive transduction)
Schizophyllum commune, 3
Schizosaccharomyces pombe, 10, 28
  auxotrophic mutants, 10
    adenine-1 (*ad-1*), 60–61, 97
    ad-6, 36, 94–95, 97
    ad-7, 91
    ad-8, 97
Secondary homothallism, 6
Segregation in fungal diploids, 9

Subunits of proteins
  identical, 42–43, 66–67, 71, 73
  nonidentical, 41, 43, 102
Suppressor mutations, 36, 92

Temperature-sensitive mutants (*see* Bacteriophage T4)
Tetrahymena phosphatases, 119
Thalassemia, 126
Thermolability of complementation products, 44, 48–49, 50, 71–72
Transconformation in enzymes, 82–83
Transcription, 51–52
Transduction, 12–15
  (*see also* Abortive transduction)
Translation, 51–52
Tryptophan synthetase, of *Escherichia coli,* 13, 30–31, 41, 72
  protein A, 11, 90
  protein B, 31
  of *Neurospora,* 56–57, 62–63, 68, 70
Tyrosinase (of *Neurospora*) 121

Uredinales (rust fungi), 5
Ustilaginales (smut fungi), 5
Ustilago maydis, 10

X chromosome, 2

Yeast (*see Saccharomyces, Schizosaccharomyces*)

Zea mays, 21
  A locus, 21–22
  catalase, 119
  esterase, 78, 119
  heterosis, 113–114
  R locus, 21